DAB & ~~DAB+~~
the Future of Radio

a digital part of the *World of Radio*

DAB & DAB+ The Future of Radio

Published by World of Radio, HU10 7TL, England

Although every precaution has been taken in preparation of this book, the publisher and author assume no responsibility for errors and omissions. Neither is any liability assumed or accepted for damages resulting from the use of the information contained herein.

First Edition. Dec 2020

ISBN. Softback: 978-1-900401-24-1

To my wife Anne

for her unstinting help and support

and to the radio pioneers who devised DAB and DAB+ making it possible for more radio expansion.

DAB & DAB+ The Future of Radio

INTRODUCTION

This book is designed to explain what DAB is, how it differs from traditional, analogue forms of radio broadcasting and its likely place in the media firmament of the future. The book reviews the development of digital radio and explains how DAB differ from other digital standards, *DRM* and *HD Radio*. The major differences between legacy DAB and DAB+, rapidly becoming the standard in most markets, are explained.

With any scientific, and particularly electronic subject, engineers often attempt to explain the subject with copious amounts of mathematics and complex theories. This book is however aimed at the layman and, while some background of certain decisions might foster a better understanding of the subject, it's beyond the scope of this work. Complex algebraic formulae and calculations have been summarised as far as possible, to make the subject easy to understand.

By Autumn 2020 there were over six hundred small-scale radio stations broadcasting in half a dozen European countries, including 221 in the UK. Denmark, France, Germany, Poland and Switzerland all have small scale DAB stations, bursting with creative people, finding new ways of engaging and delighting audiences in ways which the SSDAB technology has enabled.

Over half of all listening in the UK is to digital radio (of all types – DAB, Online, DTT, etc) and over two thirds of that listening is to DAB stations. DAB is carried on 3 national, 10 regional, 51 local and 10 'small scale' multiplexes. By the end of 2020, they were carrying 600 different radio stations. Several hundred more stations are likely to be licensed during 2021, bringing the total number to over 1,000. This book explains the DAB system, how it works and how it developed in the UK.

CONTENTS

1. WHAT IS DAB?...7

2. TECHNICAL 9

3. CHANNELS & FREQUENCIES 30

4. HISTORY 34

5. GEOGRAPHY 43

6. DAB RECEIVERS 60

7. UK DAB STATIONS...72

8. LUMINARIES & LEADERS...99

9. SUPPLIERS 110

10.   EPILOGUE 115

11.   GLOSSARY 116

ACKNOWLEDGEMENTS

I'm particularly indebted to the staff at the UK regulator OFCOM, and those at WorldDAB, for their help in checking the information. Sincere thanks to those who inspired me to write this book and gave so freely of their time, providing invaluable information, particularly my friends at many radio stations too numerous to list, to Dr Lawrie Hallett of *Opendab*, Alan Beech of *Commtronix*, Rash Mustapha and Ken 'Eagle-eyes' Baird of *dx-archive.org*.

Paul Rusling

1. What is DAB?

DAB is a standard of 'digital radio'. We shall first consider what is Digital radio and how it differs from other techniques used in radio broadcasting.

Digital Audio Broadcasting is simply a common standard of technical parameters, that certain broadcast stations use for transmission. By adhering to this technical standard, listeners can receive the station on standard radio receivers, available to buy retail. If standards were not set and stuck to, many different parameters would be used and listeners would have to have "multi-standard' receivers capable of resolving the signals before turning them back into audio.

There are several different standards of digital radio; the best known and most prevalent are **DAB, DRM** and **HDRadio**, which are described below.

DAB & DAB+ The Future of Radio

DAB is the standard used in several countries, although not in North America where a different standard has been adopted. That is called HD Radio – a trademarked term for an "in-band, on-channel" system which can be used on the AM and FM bands to transmit several different programmes down the same transmitter and on the same frequency.

This book is about the particular standard of Digital Radio called DAB – Digital Audio Broadcasting. In a literal sense, the other versions of Digital Radio could also be called DAB too. To avoid confusion, only this standard is referred to in this book as DAB. This book focuses on the 'European' type of DAB and only mentions HD Radio and DRM for comparison, explanation and clarification.

World DAB Forum's website describes DAB as:

Digital Audio Broadcasting (DAB) is designed for delivery of high-quality digital audio programmes and data services for mobile, portable and fixed reception from terrestrial transmitters in the Very High Frequency (VHF) frequency bands.

The DAB system is designed to provide spectrum and power efficient techniques in terrestrial transmitter network planning, known as the Single Frequency Network (SFN) and the gap-filling technique. The DAB system meets the required sharing criteria with other radiocommunication services.

DAB is the most widespread terrestrial broadcast digital radio standard offering broadcasters to enhance their radio offerings, to meet the higher quality expectations of listeners and to reduce energy consumption.

2. TECHNICAL

In this book, we have deliberately avoided the overly complex mathematics of radio engineering; you won't need any algebraic skills, or knowledge of integration to understand the basic principles involved in DAB radio.

RADIO WAVES

Radio waves are type of electro-magnetic radio and are considered to radiate omnidirectionally from their source (unless focussed into a beam, but that's a very complicated discussion). All Electro-magnetic waves (from radio up to visible light) are considered to travel at the same speed, around 300,000 metres per second; that's close to the figure for a vacuum and it varies with the density and composition of the air they travel through.

DAB & DAB+ The Future of Radio

ELECTRO-MAGNETIC SPECTRUM

The electro-magnetic spectrum runs from a few cycles all the way up to many Exahertz (10^{18}), Gamma waves, whose frequencies are seriously long numbers. One Exahertz is one quintillion Hertz, that's with 18 zeros on the end! The ones we deal most often in radio are only a few hundred Megahertz for DAB – a mere six zeros on the end, i.e. of the order of 200,000,000 hertz (or cycles).

The numbers used in radio engineering can be quite mind-boggling in terms of size and quantum.

First, the units. a frequency can be expressed as cycles, which is simple to understand but scientific convention is that we call cycles by the name of HERTZ, after the German scientist Heinrich Hertz who was the first to prove the existence of electromagnetic waves.

For many years, radio frequencies were names in cycles, or practice this meant kilocycles or megacycles, as the number of cycles was in the thousands or millions. Those terms have now been superseded by Hertz, thus we now have

KHz KiloHertz | **MHz** MegaHertz | **GHz** GigaHertz

It is important to have a good overview of where in the spectrum various bands are. Wavelength and frequency are often confused; each are a reciprocal function of the other. The wavelength (called by the Greek letter λ - *lambda*) is the distance a wave travels before it repeats the cycle, while frequency is the rate of repetition. Divide either into the speed of electro-magnetic radiation and you get the other.

The higher frequency bands (and thus shorter wavelength) are much broader and can accommodate more signals, but such signals do not reach so far as the wavelength gets smaller.

FREQUENCY BANDS.

The properties of radio waves vary according to their frequency, and groups of them are arranged into bands, according to how the spectrum is divided up between the various users – broadcast, mobile, astronomy, shipping, etc. The best known in broadcast radio terms are Medium Wave, Short Wave and the VHF broadcast Band II (88 to 108 MHz) and we shall now introduce you to a new one – VHF Band III, which is the main one used for DAB.

Frequency (Hertz)	Band	Use	Wavelength (metres)
20 KiloHz	Extremely Low F	Global comms	15,000 m
100 KiloHz	Super Low F	Continental comms	3000 m
200 KiloHz	Long Wave	Continental Broadcast	1500 m
1000 KiloHz	Medium Wave	National Broadcast	300 m
2000 KiloHz	Short Wave	International	150 m
30 MegaHz	Short Wave	Broadcast	10 m
50 MegaHz	VHF Band 1	TV	6 m
100 MegaHz	VHF Band II	FM	3 m
200 MegaHz	**VHF Band III.**	**DAB**	**1.5 m**
750 MegaHz	UHF Bands IV & V	Television & mobile phones	40 cm
1.5 GigaHz	**L Band**	**DAB**	**20 cm**
2 GigaHz	S BAND	Sirius	10 cm
2.4 GigaHz	S Band	WiFi LANs	12 cm
30 GigaHz	Microwaves	Communications links	1 cm
430 TeraHz	Visible light	Red	700 nm
800 TeraHz	Visible light	Violet	380 nm
30 PetaHz	Ultra Violet Light		100 nm
300 PetaHz	X Rays	Medical & imaging	5 nm
300 ExaHz	Gamma Rays	Sterilisation	100 pm

This table is simplified and omits many other spectrum users, such as communications, beacons, amateur users, etc. The frequencies are typical and do not show the limits of bands. The BOLD rows highlight the bands allocated for DAB:

VHF Band III (174 – 240 MHz)

L Band (1.452 to 1.492 GHz).

In the above discussion, we considered only a single radio signal for simplicity. In fact, if we look more closely at it (which we can, using a spectrum analyser - a screen which shows by a waveform the shape of the radio wave) we see that the radio signal isn't just a single frequency, but is a number of closely adjacent frequencies.

If we just transmit a bare signal, that is called a CARRIER and that will be just one frequency. Once we add information to the carrier, such as music or data, the carrier immediately has SIDEBANDS – which is known as the modulation.

MODULATION

On the following pages we look closely at the various different types of modulation – starting with the oldest, analogue types and then moving into the world of Digital, such as DAB.

There are several different ways of adding the programme or the modulation onto a transmitter's carrier wave. Each has their advantages, and some methods have disadvantages.

Basically, analogue sounds are continuous waves of audio, or other information, such as our voices in the air, or musical instruments. This is sound at its purest - its "full-fat" audio with a range of the basic sounds and harmonics.

Using very fast signal processing, it was discovered that any signal, audio or data, can be reduced by selectively chopping out large chunks of the signal that don't add much to its intelligence. This is called DIGITAL or digitising the signal. It is literally chopping it up into slices, which can then be transmitted more easily and cheaply. Another attraction is that it can be STORED more cheaply. Digital Radio signals are not a continuous stream of information; the information is being rapidly interrupted, as with digital audio (e.g. CDs).

AM AMPLITUDE MODULATION

When radio broadcasting began in 1920, the programme was added to the carrier by varying the level of the signal up and down, in sympathy with the audio.

AM modulated signals can be easily demodulated and converted back into regular audio by the very simplest of circuits, including the legendary 'Cats Whisker' tuners which have only three rudimentary components. The simplest radio ever was soon improved by adding powered circuits using thermionic valves, enabling loudspeakers to be used.

FM FREQUENCY MODULATION

Just before WWII, several inventors developed a new system of modulation in which the actual frequency was varied in sympathy with the audio. Frequency Modulation was applied at a much lower level in the transmitter chain and, after field tests, was found to have several advantages.

The most useful of these was that it was not so prone to interference – particularly from pulses caused by car ignition systems and other nearby electrical equipment. As most interference is amplitude based, it is not difficult to use a simple limiter to reduce the noise, leaving only frequency variations, which can then be demodulated leaving a 'cleaner' audio signal.

FM is not perfect however, having wide sidebands and also needing a more complex demodulator. The band used for FM broadcasting (around 100MHz) is prone to incoming interference from thousands of miles away with certain atmospheric conditions, such as high atmospheric pressure.

PM   PHASE MODULATION

Phase modulation is similar to frequency modulation and is an important technique in the transmission of data. It is similar to FM; both PM and FM can be considered derivatives of angular modulation however, a discussion of this involves complex mathematics and theory, which is beyond the scope of this book. In PM, the phase of the transmitter's carrier is varied in sympathy with the audio (or data). *Frequency Shift Keying* is a commonly used form of phase modulation which has been in use for many decades.

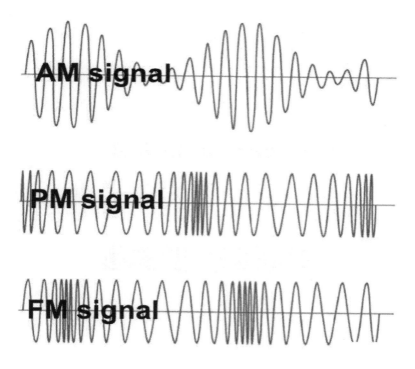

DAB & DAB+ The Future of Radio

DIGITISATION

By slicing each signal into a digital image of the analogue programme, many more audio channels can share one transmitter. The simultaneous use of one channel by two or more programmes is called *multiplexing*. This can be achieved in analogue, and many FM stations in the USA carrier extra channels in their subcarriers but is much more effectively done using digital modes of modulation.

Marconi developed a **PDM** (Pulse Duration Modulation) system in the 1970s for powerful AM transmitters. This was known as PULSAM, one of the first steps towards digital. PDM and **Delta Modulation** are simply ways of converting an audio signal into digital. Decoding a PDM signal back into analogue needs only to pass it through a low pass filter.

By sharing, or multiplexing, signals more efficient use is made of the spectrum allocated. DAB signals are coded individually in the transmitter, before being multiplexed with other programme services and data. The multiplexer output is transposed to the appropriate radio frequency band, amplified and transmitted by antennas to the coverage area.

At the receiver, the appropriate carrier frequency is tuned in. The receiver selects this carrier (and its accompanying sidebands) and the output is fed into an 'OFDM demodulator' and channel decoder, which eliminates transmission errors. The output information is then passed to the receiver's audio sections and amplified to drive loudspeakers, playing the audio of the programme.

OFDM is Frequency Division Multiplex. A way of spreading a signal over multiple (typically several 1000), closely spaced carrier frequencies, such that if one frequency is subject to interference, the signal can be successfully recovered and reconstructed from the remaining carriers. It is most commonly used for DAB, DRM and Digital TV systems.

DIGITAL TRANSMISSION

In digital transmission, the signal is switched on and off in quick succession, creating a series of zeros and ones, which represent either on or off. By using an optimum coding method of converting the audio, video or data into a digital signal, considerable efficiencies can be made, especially by discarding information not needed for intelligence.

There are many advantages and potential benefits to digital radio but for many years these were hindered by a lack of global agreement on standards.

Digital transmission requires less power than analogue, so it is more cost-effective and environmentally friendly.

There are many different forms of digital transmission, and different levels of encoding and compressing audio, drawn up by the *Moving Picture Experts Group*. The development of the MP3 format was done mainly by the *Fraunhofer Society*, a global network of scientists, whose UK base is at the Strathclyde University.

MPEG are a working group of authorities representing the fields of audio, TV, radio and video. They developed various standards for audio, which are known as MP2, MP3, AAC. There are others, such as Orbis, FLAC, Vorbis, etc. each of the audio coding formats has a standard or specification and it is known as an **audio codec**.

DAB & DAB+ The Future of Radio

Digital Audio Broadcasting has now been under development for forty years. As such, it is a very mature format and some even claim that it is now obsolete as it has been surpassed and superseded by DAB+. The history of the evolvement of the modes is discussed in Chapter Four.

DAB's encoding system uses a system of compression called MP2. The European patents for the DAB standards expired on 18th January 2013 and DAB is now a 'free-to-integrate' technology. DAB transmissions are not compatible with analogue transmissions and have their own band of frequencies. Two bands have been allocated for DAB, the Band III VHF band from 174 to 240 MHz, previously used for TV in many countries, and the L Band, which extends from 1.452 to 1.492 GHz. Band III VHF is the most popular, whereas the L band offers more space for expansion of future services.

DAB/DAB+ was originally conceived just for the local VHF band III, when it becomes vacant or partially vacant. It's not possible to use the DAB standards in other bands, such as Medium Wave or short wave, which offer wide area coverage. DAB transmissions are therefore limited to only short range coverage and would need hundreds of transmitters to cover the same area that lower frequencies can reach.

For DAB+, a more efficient coding method is used which adds an extra layer of correction based on Reed-Solomon encoding placed around the byte interleaved audio frame but inside the coding of the DAB system, increasing its ruggedness.

Due to its high efficiency encoding (AAC version 2 compared to MPEG-1 Layer 2 for DAB) the impact of lost bits would be greater, so all bits are protected equally. This means that when the signal gets too weak, audio frames are lost and the audio mutes. This is indicated by CRC errors only, as the failure point is much sharper than for DAB.

DAB & DAB+ The Future of Radio

DAB+ (DAB Plus)

There were many criticism of the DAB standard in the early years of the 21st century and so many alterations were made to it. Some of the concerns were over the sheer cost and bandwidth the DAB system used. The only countries where DAB began to have any traction was the UK and Denmark, but even there, progress was very slow, needing the regulator to use a stick to beat radio stations to use DAB.

The DAB standard received a complete upgrade in 2006 which resulted in DAB+. One of the biggest changes was made possible by adopting the use of the AAC coding standard for DAB+. The AAC standard gives higher fidelity and sound quality than MP3 and certainly better than the MP2 used by the DAB system. AAC and the DAB+ standard is also much more efficient, meaning less 'space' is taken for a programme, enabling the transmission provider operating the multiplex to squeeze more stations onto a transmission.

The biggest problem to the changeover to DAB+ is that the technology was not forward compatible; i.e. older sets could not usually be upgraded to the new DAB+ system. For the countries which had the largest number of DAB receivers in use, this proved a difficult pill to swallow – their DAB technology was being made obsolete. The possibility was hushed up, especially in the UK and some sectors hoped they could bulldoze the UK into an 'all-DAB' landscape. The British radio industry kept a silence about DAB+, even as the new system was being adopted by other countries.

New radios that can receive both DAB and DAB+ transmissions often have a 'tick-mark' added to them. To use DAB+, a licence fee must be paid to the rights holders of the AAC. A royalty of less than $1 per receiver is levied by the rights holder to the aac+ coding, represented by VIA Licensing of San Francisco and their UK agents, *Commtronix*.

DRM   Digital Radio Mondiale.

A set of standards specifically designed to work with and alongside existing analogue transmissions on all bands, including AM, Short Wave and the FM broadcast band at 88 to 108MHz. DRM uses the spectrum allocated to it far more efficiently than AM or FM and uses an AAC based coding format. In tests in 2020, DRM was found to have the lowest carbon footprint, for transmission and reception.

DRM for mediumwave has been tested and documented about two decades ago. It has been recommended by ITU in 2005 and all the tests carried out all over the world are available openly and freely for anyone to see.

Moreover, 35 stations, soon to be increased to 41, in India, are on the air every single day. Their coverage is about 800 million people. Seven radio manufacturers have receivers in the market, although these are rarely seen in radio shops.

In radio, bandwidth is the limiting factor, so DRM uses computer processing power to make the most of the spectrum available. Two channels plus limited data is normally broadcast in the DRM and enhancements to the DRM-FM standard allow six extra channels using an existing channel and antenna.

Only 40% of the power is needed to achieve the same coverage, with far better fidelity. The BBC are launching a DRM pilot on the Medium Wave band to serve the Middle East in 2021 from its Cyprus transmission base. Over a quarter of listeners to the World Service still use AM and it is expected that the DRM service should achieve good penetration in the volatile Levant region. In Russia, China and many other countries the demand for Short Wave is still healthy.

HDRadio is an "in-band, on-channel" digital system that can be used on any traditional broadcast band, including medium wave or FM. There are hybrid system that enable *HDRadio* to use the same facilities as existing stations. HDRadio can use a single frequency to transmit up to six channels of programme in clear sound. The system also provides some capacity for data which can be used to send text or pictures to the listeners. Bit Rates used are from 48 kbps on AM to 128 kbps on the FM band.

HDRadio is becoming well-established in many major cities across North America where there are car, home and portable radio receivers readily available. Over 250 models of car now come with HD Radio installed and over 4,000 stations on air already, serving over 50 million radios in cars and around 15m in homes and offices. In Autumn 2020 the FCC gave permission for all AM stations to go 'all digital' if they wish; previously only two stations had tried this radical step.

When an HD Radio tuner loses the station's digital signal, it will automatically switch over to the analogue signal broadcast at the same frequency. There may be a slight break in the sound when this happens. When the tuner is back in range of a station's HD Radio signal, it will automatically revert to the digital broadcast.

HD Radio technology has been implemented in over 2,400 radio stations around the world, reaching over 400 million listeners in countries as diverse as the USA, Mexico, Canada and India. HD Radio technology was developed, and continues to be licensed by, *iBiquity Digital Corporation*. It has been suggested by some industry commentators that a major reason for HD radio technology is to offer some limited digital radio services while preserving the value of the existing radio stations.

ONLINE RADIO

A field on its own, Online Radio is universally available in every part of the world (though some countries limit the access for political reasons) and offers over 100,000 'stations'. Often called 'internet radio', Online radio is growing rapidly. There are some costs to the listener – the cost of the internet connection, whereas *DAB, DAB+, DRM* and *HDRadio* are 'free to air'. Online radio is digital and listening to it is usually lumped in with DAB in listening surveys.

DTT
(Digital Terrestrial Television)

In late 2002, the Digital TV transmitters in the UK began carrying radio services on their spare capacity. The BBC launched their newer DAB-only channels along with *BBC Asian* and the *BBC World Service.* Some months later they added their main channels, simulcasting AM & FM outlets.

EMAP also launched *Smash, Kerrang* and *Kiss* while fellow commercial stations *OneWord* and *JazzFM* also debuted. There has been some churn and shuffling from one TV multiplex to another. There are now almost thirty radio stations broadcasting on the DTT multiplexes. They all transmit 'free to air' and can be found on virtual channels in the 700 range.

In many parts of the UK, up to FIVE additional radio channels can be found on channels 719 to 722, and channel 735. At the moment these are all the BBC's network of local radio stations and they are grouped regionally, so that in any area, the nearest five stations that can be heard in that particular BBC region can be found. For example, in the 'BBC North' area of Yorkshire, the BBC local stations on DTT are *Radios Sheffield, York, Leeds, Humberside* and *Lincoln.* In the three nations of Scotland, Wales and Northern Ireland, listeners can find their own national stations, *e.g. Radio Wales, Radio Cymru, Radio Ulster, etc.*

DAB & DAB+ The Future of Radio

DSR Digital Satellite Radio

Satellite has offered listeners radio channels on the sub-carriers of various channels since the 1980s. Many of these were carried on the Astra birds, each analogue channel could carry up to five radio stations. The receivers were not easy to set up and were fixed, needing a satellite dish to receive the signals. This limited the appeal and the take up of satellite radio.

In Europe, both Eutelsat and the Astra birds carried many hundreds of channels of radio stations, and these were relied on for feeding remote transmitters, as well as for feeds to cable head-ends.

Even the transfer of satellite services to digital didn't help much, although the extra space for services has brought the costs down dramatically and made it possible for many more stations to broadcast on satellite., although it has become primarily used for distribution. The old problems of needing a dish to see the bird's signal are still a problem

In the USA two networks built satellites which offered radio signals as a primary service, and at higher power level. More importantly, the American radio satellites operate at much lower frequencies than the TV satellites that service northern Europe do.

The Astra 'direct to home' satellites, as used by SKY and Freeview, use frequencies around 12 GHz, but a lot of American radio satellites are around 2.3 GHz (the 'S' band) and even 1GHz, the 'L' band. These are migrating towards higher frequencies as power capabilities increase and the bands get more congested.

DAB & DAB+ The Future of Radio

The lower latitudes of most of the USA means the signals received from satellites are stronger than receivers in northern latitudes, such as the UK. Stronger signals need simpler antennas, meaning that its possible to use omnidirectional receiving antennas on cars and enjoy reasonably consistent broadcast reception.

XM Satellite and **Sirius** each launched services and their offer of about 80 channels was carefully coordinated with the availability of in-dash receivers in cars. They had to fight opposition from existing terrestrial radio stations to get the FCC to release suitable frequencies to start the services. The services were on a subscription basis, but many motorists are prepared to pay the modest monthly fees (about $10) for a good service. Sirius and XM merged in 2008 in a deal valued at $3.3 billion. The resulting **SiriusXM Radio** had 18m subscribers by that time, a number they have since doubled.

Worldspace

Established as an international organisation, Worldspace began broadcasting radio programmes to Europe, Africa and the Middle East in 1999 from a pair of satellites. At its peak, Worldspace attracted almost 200,000 subscribers in Africa and almost half a million in Asia – 95% of those being in India. To attract new customers, and donations for its charitable work, *Worldspace* gave space to *Radio Caroline*, offering it a near-global coverage.

The company never achieved the penetration it needed to make it commercially viable despite offering 62 channels of programmes. Two thirds of the channels were provided by other, independent suppliers such as *Radio Caroline* and two dozen channels were originated 'in house'. In late 2008, Worldspace closed its plush London office and the following year it filed for bankruptcy, owing over $50 million. Two years later, founder Noah Samara was part of a management buy-out of the company for just $5m but the plan to redevelop it as an educational tool has not yet happened.

DAB & DAB+ The Future of Radio

DAB – the Principles.

All naturally made audio originates as analogue signals – our voices and musical instruments for example. It was discovered that these could be digitised , so they could be moved electronically as a series of ones and zeros. This made it possible to remove many unnecessary parts of the audio, and focus transmission on the important intelligence-bearing parts of a signal. The efficiencies are many and complex.

A DAB audio signal is encoded in MP2 , which is an standard for encoding audio digitally. It was the forerunner of MP3, which became a *defacto* standard when popularised by the Apple iPod around 2000 and on other audio players.

A DAB+ audio signal is encoded in **aacPlus** (its full name is aacPlus HE v2) which is the ancestor to the MP3 format. Mobile audio devices such iPods use AAC as standard. The aacPlus standard uses a number of clever techniques to make it more efficient, so the audio sounds better at lower bitrates than DAB with inferior its MP2 audio.

<u>48kbps DAB+ sounds similar to a 128kbps DAB signal</u>.

DAB+ audio signals also have slightly improved error correction, which can mean a reduction in 'bubbling mud' or other problems in poor reception areas.

Apart from that, there are no differences. DAB+ and DAB use the same transmitters, same multiplexing equipment, and so on, and DAB and DAB+ signals can happily live on the same DAB multiplex. A DAB+ radio will also happily decode DAB signals as well (although a DAB radio won't decode DAB+).

Almost every DAB radio on sale today will cope with DAB+ automatically or will prompt you with instructions on how to upgrade (which could be as easy as typing a code in or downloading some new firmware).

ADVANTAGES OF DAB

National DAB networks cover most major towns and most motorways and major roads. The DAB transmissions reach more than 9 out of 10 people in Britain and further expansion is ongoing to match the FM coverage achieved, though that is below 100%.

A variety of local digital radio networks are also on air, meaning you can usually listen to the BBC and larger commercial stations on DAB too.

Cost

Unlike TV, there is no need for a licence to receive DAB programmes. Once you buy a receiver, there are no ongoing costs other than power, whether main or battery. The programmes are received 'free to air'.

Plenty of room for everyone

The migration of DAB to higher frequencies means there is more space for more transmitters, plus by sharing the transmitter among several stations, more channels or stations can be carried by each transmitter. By broadcasting in mono and cutting down the data rates, up to thirty stations can be accommodated on one transmitter.

While there is room for everyone, building a network of transmitters costs serious money, demanding hefty investment by Arqiva and other mux operators with little guarantee of a return. The regulator, OFCOM, put into place a system where the Multiplex operator (mux operator – e.g. Arqiva) is effectively a gatekeeper and only carries the programmes of the stations able to afford its fees, which can be very high. Traditionally this was reflected in carriage fees.

National coverage was for some time limited to stations owned and operated by the big radio groups, predominantly those owned by Arqiva's biggest customers – Global and Bauer.

DAB & DAB+ The Future of Radio

Names, not Numbers
DAB digital radio displays the stations by name. That gives you the confidence to explore the airwaves and change stations at the touch of a button.

No Interference
Although DAB is capable of CD quality, the cost of bitrate and capacity determines the quality of audio, and many services fall well short of CD quality. It is somewhat ridiculous that the marketing men still freely use the term "CD quality" after 20 years of often anything but CD quality.

New Features
Digital radios have screens that can show more information about what you're listening to. This could be the title and artist of the song, the news headlines, or the latest sports results, though it does depend on the station operator – some don't seem to use the facility well at all.

Slideshows
Most DAB receivers have a screen, which is primarily used to illustrate which radio station is being received. Slideshows enable a station to add synchronised visual content (slides) to broadcasts which enhances the listener experience. The visuals use standard web image formats and standard web publishing tools.

Slides can be shown at any frame rate, from 1 frame per second upwards. Much faster frame rates (up to 10fps) are supported through use of APNG (Animated PNG) files which can give an illusion of animation similar to "Flash" on websites. DAB receivers that can't support animation will revert to displaying a still image when displaying an APNG file.

Slideshow's specification allows for 64 images (or 450kBytes) to be cached on the receiver. This means the station can pre-send slides in the background and trigger them accurately when required for display.

DAB & DAB+ The Future of Radio

DAB DISADVANTAGES

Power Consumption. Due to the complexity of DAB circuitry, more power is consumed than a traditional AM or FM one. While not a problem for mains driven sets, or in a vehicle, a battery powered one will run down batteries quickly.

Weak Signal. DAB is broadcast at higher frequencies than FM – over twice the frequency around 200 MHz, so they do not travel so far. They're absorbed and reflected by such topological features as trees and buildings, diminishing the signals at the receiver. Weak signal can be negated by the use of infill transmitters, which are easy to implement with the SFN (single frequency network) technology.

Sound fidelity With DAB, weak *correction coding** stopping the received signal from correcting errors being received, which led to the 'bubbling mud' effects, even in strong signal areas. In weak signal areas this was a particular problem in the early years of DAB. When the wanted signal is close to a stronger one, this can be worse, often with no signal received.

> * *Forward error correction,* aka 'channel coding' is a technique for ensuring the information is error free, usually achieved by duplicating some or all of the signal.

Cost. The costs of DAB have been very high, particularly in the UK. The cost for carriage even on a local multiplex is approaching £100,000 a year. The high costs of DAB monopoly gatekeepers could be reduced by Small Scale DAB mux operators, to around a half or even third the figures being charged on the legacy multiplexes.

Legacy DAB stations resorted to low bitrate mono to keep costs low and maximise the number of stations on a multiplex (typically around 15). Using DAB+ with its AAC coding, up to 30 stereo stations can use one multiplex, reducing costs significantly.

DAB & DAB+ The Future of Radio

BIT RATES

The amount of data transmitted has an effect on the audio quality of the programme, but it also takes up less space on the multiplex and so can be cheaper for radio stations to transmit. The listener too also benefits from lower bitrates as the signal can be more robust. Many internet carriers limit the amount of data per month.

While not so data hungry as movies or maps, audio can still consume a lot of data, so it is usually better to use the lowest bit rate tolerable. A 128k stream uses around 1MB of mobile data per minute, or 60MB per hour. The average listener in the UK tunes in for 23 hours a week, so the data consumed soon racks up, as can the costs! Those paying for internet by the amount of data carried will be disadvantaged, however as DAB radio delivers the data free, this is a key advantage.

The typical bitrate for DAB stereo programs is 128 kbit/s or less, and as a result, giving a lower sound quality than FM, prompting complaints from audiophiles. That original 'standard' stream of 128kbps for a DAB signal can be cut to only a third, i.e. 48kbps, by using the DAB+ system (AAC). This means that it is about three times more efficient than 'old skool' DAB for a very similar sounding audio.

The BBC transmits its primary national services as a 'Joint Stereo' signal at 320 kbps on its *Sounds* online service. On its DAB mux, it reduces most of these down to 128 kbps, or 192 in the case of Radio 3. The channels that carry mainly speech are transmitted at 80 and even 64kbps.

The main commercial radio stations transmit at 64 and 128 online, while on DAB these are reduced to 24/32/40/64 and 80 kbps with Classic FM using 128kbps. Many of the commercial services are mono only. Many online radio stations offer lower bit-rate streams for listeners to select, if they wish. This enables them to keep their data demand down and save cost, especially on mobile phones.

DAB & DAB+ The Future of Radio

Even by stepping down the quality and transmitting a mono signal at a lower rate, stations retain almost all their listeners, proving that people select a radio station for its programme, rather than audio fidelity. This is very similar to listeners choosing to listen to an AM station rather than FM, if AM offered the programme they wanted and FM didn't. Listener choice will always rule!

Some query the success of mono stations but it should be remembered that many listeners have only a one speaker radio, especially those listening on a smart speaker. Once again – content wins hands down over quality, every time.

Some of the fastest growing radio stations use very low bits rates. Union Jack is a local station that programmes only British Music (it launched in the wake of the Brexit referendum, in 2016) and it uses only a 32kbps mono signal. But managed to increase its listening by 73% in 2018. Some stations use mono streams at just 32kbps which is very economical.

Many of the latest radio stations now meeting with substantial success are in mono only: *Absolute 90s, Heart Extra, Heat, Kiss, Planet Rock, Radio X and Smooth* for example.

NOTE.
Manipulation of bitrates and over-frugality led to a lot of the criticism of DAB.

The actual rates that the data requires for transmission are:

	MPEG2 DAB	HE-AAC DAB+
'Better than FM'	192 - 256	56 - 96
'Similar to FM'	160 - 192	40 - 64
'Acceptable,	128 - 160	24 - 48

(based on stereo signals)

3. Channels & Frequencies

The national regulators interested in DAB broadcasting agreed on a plan for the VHF Band III frequencies at a conference in Wiesbaden, Germany. The framework agreed was to channelise the band, which runs from 175 to 240 MHz. The currently plan has broadly retained the old channel numbers used for TV in some countries, such as the UK, and divide these into subchannels, which are called A,B,D and D. Channel 13 is divided into six, as the table opposite shows.

The international agreement for DAB (held in Wiesbaden) suggested that blocks 11B to 12D would be used for DAB in the UK. Extra allocations using the other channels have since been agreed as other users, such as Private Mobile Radio and stage microphones, have been moved from Band III.

The BBC National services use channel 12B, which is centred on 225.648MHz. The BBC uses around 400 transmitter sites to get its DAB service to listeners, achieving coverage of over 97% of the population, though somewhat less in terms of geographical area covered. There are plans for more "fill in" transmitters. Geographically, the coverage is about 77% of the UK's land mass.

The BBC's network carries only BBC services, some of them at very high data rates such as BBC Radio 3 which is transmitted at 192 kbit/s, whereas its talk channels (Radio 4 and Radio 5) use only 64 kbps and are transmitted in mono, saving more space.

DAB & DAB+ The Future of Radio

Frequencies used by DAB transmitters in Band III

Block	Label	Frequency	MUX
13	5A	174.928	
14	5B	176.640	
15	5C	178.352	
16	5D	180.064	
17	6A	181.936	
18	6B	183.648	
19	6C	185.360	
20	6D	187.072	
21	7A	188.928	
22	7B	190.640	
23	7C	192.352	
24	7D	194.064	**SS** (Small Scale)
25	8A	195.936	SS
26	8B	197.648	SS
27	8C	199.360	
28	8D	201.072	
29	9A	202.928	**SS**
30	9B	204.640	SS
31	9C	206.352	SS
32	9D	208.064	
33	10A	209.936	
34	10B	211.648	**SS & Local**
35	10C	213.360	**Local**
36	10D	215.072	**Local**
37	11A	216.928	**SDR National**
38	11B	218.640	**Local**
39	11C	220.352	**Local** & SS
40	11D	222.064	**D1 National**
41	12A	223.936	**D1 Scotland** & SS
42	12B	225.648	**BBC National**
43	12C	227.360	**Local** (Ireland)
44	12D	229.072	**Local**
45	13A	230.784	
46	13B	232.496	
47	13C	234.208	
48	13D	235.776	
49	13E	237.488	
50	13F	239.200	

COMMERCIAL DAB ENSEMBLES

There are a number of commercial DAB multiplexes operators in the UK who run 48 local and regional DAB ensembles (multiplexes) across the United Kingdom. These include the two national operators, **Digital One** and **Sound Digital** as well as local multiplex operators including NOW Digital, Bauer Media Group, the Wireless Group, Switch Digital and MuxCo.

TESTS.

Licenses are occasionally issued for stations to radiate signals for development purposes. They're usually on Block 9B & 10C but are not intended for public listening.

L BAND.

Under a Maastricht plan in 2002, the UK and the rest of Europe was also authorised to use L band allocations for local terrestrial DAB, though currently there are no plans to broadcast any digital radio stations on the L band. The last broadcast users of the L band were *Worldspace*, whose L band frequencies used several dozen channels. (See Page 23)

OFCOM auctioned spectrum in L band in 2008 for a number of uses, including terrestrial digital radio. *Qualcomm* (a multi-national company based in California) won the auction but have not so far brought it into use, except for test transmissions for development purposes. Arqiva made transmissions in Cambridge in 2005 from a site at Milton on the LA Block (1452.960MHz) and in London on the LP Block (1478.640 MHz) but these ceased in 2009.

The L band is used for several other services , long range RADAR and satellite links. The **Iridium** satellite network uses frequencies on the edge of L Band for its global satellite mobile phone network. The name Iridium was chosen as early calculations suggested that 77 satellites would be needed for global coverage – Iridium being a metal with the atomic number of 77. The network has not been successful so far, due to the large size of the mobile phones needed and heavy battery usage.

Traffic Alert Systems

For the last forty years there have been many attempts to develop an alert system to warn drivers of traffic problems. Several methods of traffic news dissemination have been tried, including **Car Fax**, **RoadData** and **Radio Data Systems** (RDS), a European standard. In the USA, RDS is known as RBDS. RDS (And others) are subcarriers of extra data sent along the same transmitter as a regular FM signal as a sub-carrier.

A basic traffic announcement on one station for its local area is known as a TA (Traffic Announcement). The **TA** facility can be switched on or off by the listener, who might not want to hear the announcements. A different facility is **TP** – Traffic Programme or Traffic Protocol. Activating this facility commands the radio to monitor ALL stations on that band and switch over to them as soon as they broadcast their TA signal, or flag as its called.

To get DAB into vehicles and avoid traffic jams, the EU introduced a directive, mandating that all new cars have a digital radio installed. This *(European Electronic Communications Code)* has considerably enhanced the prospects for DAB.

Enhanced Other Networks

EON messages suggest other nearby radio stations that the listener / driver might also get information from. The system also has a subsidiary options that allow track details to be transmitted. Some stations used this to add details such as contact information for commercials, some used it to broadcast the weather forecasts, and others used it for traffic information.

Many stations however, didn't bother adding anything, although some were restricted by their regulator in content of the sub-carriers; the UK for example. The BBC invested a lot of man-hours into adding track details of music being played on some channels.

HISTORY

A brief history of radio broadcasting

Radio dominates lives in most countries of the world. While the one eyed monster has become not only a key feature in most homes, and many places of work, and has now spread to a significant proportion of vehicles and even hand-held use with the spread of the smartphone, it is radio that still accounts for most media attention.

This is mainly due to the ability of radio listeners being able to do other things – work, commuting, etc, while simultaneously listening. TV doesn't lend itself to (ambidexterity) ; it's hard to do most things while being glued to a screen. You can't work, walk and much less drive a car while watching TV – though some have tried, often with catastrophic results!

DAB & DAB+ The Future of Radio

When audio broadcasting began around 1920 (the exact point varies between countries, thanks to licensing peculiarities) radio was made mainly on long waves and soon after on the medium wave band. Stations often shared frequencies, which were not very well controlled and regulation in some parts of the world was very light.

In the UK and some European countries, the government kept a firm hand on broadcasting. Radio frequencies were regarded by many as being far too important for a frivolous thing like broadcasting. This was shortly after the Great War and millions of men were still in military service. Electronics manufacturers were keen to promote sales of components and complete radios and many of the companies made experimental transmissions. This included the Marconi Company, Westinghouse, General Electric, Metropolitan Vickers, Westinghouse and others.

Those of the Marconi Company are the best known, and they were very active promoting the new idea of broadcasting. Promotional events were common-place such as the world-famous soprano Dame Nelly Melba singing live at their transmitter in Essex. Almost all broadcasting was live; the only recorded material was on phonographs. When these were played, the engineers simply wheeled the phonograph (they were still all-acoustic devices) up to the microphone.

By 1920, Marconi were one of the world's biggest manufacturers of communications equipment and had twenty years' experience in transmission. They allowed their staff to broadcast programmes of news, music, comedy and poetry to anyone who wished to 'listen in', as it was then called as this was felt likely to help promote sales of their equipment. London had two competing stations plus there were others in Birmingham and Manchester.

In some countries, programmes were sponsored by major newspapers or other commercial companies, but when formal applications were made for licences in the UK, the General Post Office rejected the idea. They had complete authority over all communications, including post, newspaper and radio.

DAB & DAB+ The Future of Radio

The GPO regulated all communications in the UK and, in 1922, they insisted that ALL the equipment suppliers should group together and pool resources, forming the British Broadcasting Company. This was to be funded by the biggest equipment manufacturers and a levy would be added to the sale of every radio receiver. This encouraged more people to build their own receivers and radio construction became a popular hobby in the 1920s as a result.

Radio became so important by 1926 that the government ordered that the BBC, still a private company and now with stations scattered all over the country, should be handed over to a public corporation, subsidised exclusively by the radio receiver licence fees. The BBC has operated using that model ever since.

The BBC expanded to three services: the National Programme, several regional programmes and an Empire service, which broadcast to the world on short wave. That later became the World Service and now seems to have dropped 'British' from its identity.

The world's first ever television programmes were made by John Logie Baird in 1923 who, within two years, was demonstrating television to the public in Selfridges store in London. He was soon transmitting the pictures over hundreds of miles and then across the Atlantic, using a part-mechanical method. The BBC became involved and transmitted programmes made by Baird at his own studio in south London. Those initial pictures were transmitted on Medium Wave, with the sound accompaniment on a second MW frequency.

By 1936 the BBC were sharing their transmitters between Baird and EMI, who offered a higher definition system which eventually was preferred. Baird then focussed on colour TV and had a system working by 1939 when WWII broke out and stopped radio and TV development in Europe. All experiments were focussed on the war effort, especially radar, the development of which led to dozens of small private radio manufacturers springing up.

DAB & DAB+ The Future of Radio

The Birth of FM

One of the biggest developments in broadcasting came from Edward Armstrong. He invented the regeneration and the superheterodyne circuits and then a system of adding modulation to radio waves by varying the frequency – FM was born! Previously, it had been claimed that FM was no better than AM, but by moving the frequencies ever high Armstrong was able to develop a wide-band FM which overcame the impulse noises that marred AM reception.

Armstrong conducted experiments in the RCA labs in the Empire State building but they were more interested in television so threw him out. Armstrong's demonstrations were well received by the press and by the FCC., Those first transmissions were in Band I, at 42 MHz but that was needed for television so, at the end of WWII, they were moved to Band II, 88 to 108 MHz, where they remain today.

In 1940, RCA realised that their dismissal of FM was a mistake and they offered Armstrong $1 million for his patent, but he rejected their takeover bid and there began a bitter and lengthy legal battles over the new form of transmission. He later committed suicide in New York, following which his wife accepted RCA's offer and took the $1m, although the court battles continued until 1967.

After that, FM become more popular in the USA, although many restrictive laws, such as a non-duplication rule, curtailed real growth until around 1980.   When first rolled out, FM had been the preserve of educational stations. The AM band was where the real action was, and the big profits.

Station operators would often turn to alternative outlets to use their FM allocations; the standard fare heard on the FM band was easy-listening or 'beautiful music.' often intended as background music for playing in elevators, etc.

Jazz and classical stations prevailed on the FM band, augmented by some foreign language stations, until well into the seventies. In 1967, Tom Donahue took over a daily four hour slot on a small station in San Francisco called KPMX. It usually carried programmes in foreign languages and never figured in the ratings so Donahue began programming 'alternative rock' music, which was then called 'underground'. At this time, the American music business changing rapidly and San Francisco was the place where it was all happening! Within two months, KPMX had become all underground under Donahue's control and attracted huge *avant garde* audiences.

The KPMX DJs played psychedelic and experimental music that addressed the culture of sex and drugs more openly than any previous San Francisco station. KMPX DJs adopted a mellow, laid-back style of presentation, as opposed to the breathless 100mph pace of the AM Top 40 stations. The station played album tracks instead of hit singles, a format adopted by Radio Caroline in Europe a little later.

All of a sudden, the listeners were hearing albums that they'd never heard on the radio before. This was a world first as that kind of music had not previously been heard. KPMX went more commercial and limited what could be played, but the DJs rebelled and walked out. They all wound up on another FM station, KSFR which had an all classical music format. Overnight this became THE voice of the underground, and of free speech and was reborn as KSAN.

This new counter-cultural, hippie run outlet became the most important for the music for about ten years, and showed how to be a true community station, with free access to listeners who were invited to become involved in the station's output.

Eventually, the commercial potential and political pressure overwhelmed the free-form, activist community stations. In spite of their appeal, the non-commercial segments began to disappear – KSAN, became all country music for a while.

DAB & DAB+ The Future of Radio

In the UK, FM broadcasts had begun in the 1950s, but the system didn't take off until the mid 1980s due to several factors. First, the BBC insisted on transmitting FM as horizontally polarised signals, meaning that portables and car radios got poor reception.

The BBC also kept their most popular station, Radio 1, off the FM band until the late 1980s, limiting its growth. It was a confined to an AM network shared with a megawatt station in Europe, marring its signal after dark. The BBC reluctantly made two hours of FM coverage available late at night, at a time when radio listening was at a low ebb and most pop music fans were tuned to Radio Luxembourg.

In the 1980s, dozens of unlicensed stations had begun using the FM band to broadcast a variety of formats to the capital. Some enterprising radio engineers found it was easy to put a low power FM transmitters on tower blocks and cover most of the capital. A 'cat and mouse' game ensued with the most zealous radio investigators earnestly closing the stations down and seizing the equipment. Just as quickly, replacements were put on the air from other blocks.

The regulator of commercial radio stations was instructed to try new types of smaller stations and make provision of the most popular types of music that the 'pirates' were playing. These were mainly soul music formats, and so stations such as *Kiss FM* were licensed plus others such as *Choice FM* in South London and several non-English language stations aimed at the Greek, Turkish and Asian populations.

There were hundreds of applications for the new licences and the regulator moved very slowly. Applicants had to send in dozens of copies of multipage applications, with a high 'reading' fee and many other hoops to be jumped through, including assembling a board of directors packed with the 'great and the good'. This was well beyond the capabilities of many groups and certainly not small scale radio!

DAB & DAB+ The Future of Radio

DAB HISTORY

The standard called DAB began life as a research project in 1980. The IRT (*Institute fur Rundfunk Technik - the Institute for Broadcast Technology*) tested a system with engineers from the BBC, Deutsche Welle, the NRK and other state broadcasters.

After demonstrations to the ITU's World Radio Conference in Genera in 1985, the first over the air broadcasts were made in 1988. It was known in those days as Project **Eureka 147**.

The early standards were formalised by ETSI and published in 1995 in their standard ETSI TR 101495, which was last updated in November 2019.

UK DAB TIMELINE

The first transmissions in the UK were of an experimental nature, managed by the BBC and came from the Crystal Palace transmitter in South London. Finally in 1995, the BBC began a regular service and broadcast Radios 1,2,3,4 and its new service, Radio 5. The BBC World Service and BBC Asian was also added.

New legislation the following year allowed for the licensing of the Radio Authority's three national, plus its regional and local services, to be carried on DAB. Almost all commercial radio transmitters were operated by NTL, a successor to the old IBA engineering division.

A key date to the expansion of DAB was the launch of the first car radio equipped with DAB; that was in 1997, with the first receiver costing £800. The first DAB portables were available by 1999 but were horrendously expensive and very power-hungry.

Commercial DAB

The following year, the Radio Authority (the then regulator for all non-BBC radio) offered a licence to operate a single national commercial multiplex. There was only one applicant – the GWR Group (owners of the only national commercial radio station, Classic FM)   in partnership with transmitter operator NTL. They combined to form **DIGITAL ONE**, which came on the air in the last few weeks of the 20th century.

One of the first transmissions from Digital One was a recording of birdsong, made in the Wiltshire garden of Classic FM's Chief Engineer, Quentin Howard. It had originally been made and used for the launch of INR-1, Classic FM in 1992. The birdsong channel continued on the Digital 1 multiplex for around ten years and was also used for test transmissions of Classic FM in the Netherlands and in Finland. Birdsong Radio then continued online but recently returned to the air on SS-DAB channels in Portsmouth and in Glasgow.

The commercial DAB operator was mandated to carry the three INR services (Classic FM, TalkRadio and Virgin) as one of its licence conditions. Among the programmes they carried were those of *ITN Newsradio, OneWord, Prime Time, Core Radio* and *The Groove*.

As well as being received in cars, Digital One and the BBC's national multiplex would also be picked up on the first HiFi home receivers, costing around £2,000! Within a year much cheaper radios were made available – the first sub-£100 model was the Pure Digital *Evoke* range of sets.

In the early days a number of independent organisations operated national stations, but as DAB did not become an overnight commercial success these stations fell by the wayside. They were often replaced by "flavoured sub-brands" of stations from the large groups such as Bauer and Global, who wanted to fill the capacity of the multiplexes so that the DAB landscape did not start to look like a barren wasteland.

DAB & DAB+ The Future of Radio

In the first ten years of the 21st century, *Channel Four TV* launched several stations on DAB only but, like several stations launched on regional and local muxes, didn't last long. After an experimental period of broadcasting through the night, BFBS moved onto DAB permanently, but the GCap group decided to retreat and closed down its all jazz channel and *Channel Life*.

In 2004, NTL sold its transmitters to the *Maquarie Group*, which became ARQIVA, the company that now operates all TV and most of the radio transmitters in the UK. Arqiva employ around 2,300 staff to operate the transmitters at 1,450 sites around the UK and are headquartered at the old IBA transmission park in Winchester in Hampshire. The company are now owed by a consortium of investors, led by the Canada Pension Plan.

As well as its Digital One national DAB network, Arqiva operates two dozen local multiplexes through its **NOW Digital** subsidiary.

In 2016, Sound Digital Ltd won the licence to operate the UK's second national multiplex. Arqiva were the main contractor and provider of transmission sites for the second digital network. Arqiva also provide the transmission facilities for over 90% of the local multiplexes.

arqiva

GEOGRAPHY

Of the several dozen countries where DAB has launched, the UK, Romania and Brunei are the only ones that still have a significant number of DAB transmitters in use. The majority of other countries, especially those in Europe, have converted their services to DAB+.

Countries with regular DAB services

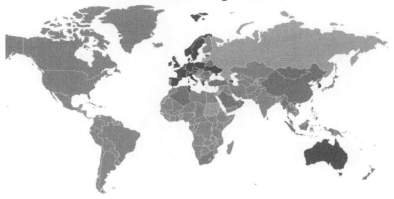

The darker shaded countries have DAB services.
Map in colour is on WorldDAB web page.
https://www.worlddab.org/countries

DAB & DAB+ The Future of Radio

The latest situation on DAB and DAB+ in various countries:

ALGERIA
DAB+ transmissions began with a single station at Tamenfoust run by the TDA (Télédiffusion d'Algérie) celebrating World Radio Day.

AUSTRALIA   The first Australian DAB+ mux launched in 2009, since when many Australian cities have been covered and more than 6 million DAB+ radios have been sold. There are over 200 stations broadcasting with DAB+ signals on 13 regional DAB networks that simulcast AM or FM, plus about 150 'exclusively DAB+' services, making a total of almost 400 stations.

The AM /FM market which has 75 stations in the five major cities. There are no format restrictions on Australian stations, which are free to vary their output to suit demand. Accountants *Price Waterhouse Cooper* are projecting that up to 4 million cars with DAB+ radios by the end of 2021.

The market has benefitted from a wave of 'pop-up' stations running for short periods which has attracted considerable attention from the public. These allow for flexible niche programming highlighting the events, such as festivals or artists. They are used primarily for broadcasting emergency service warnings during fire or the recent Queensland floods as well as for broadcasting sports or music events

AUSTRIA   A new national network of DAB+ was launched by the ORF in 2019 with coverage already being around 85%. Twenty DAB+ stations are on the air, only two are simulcasts from other bands. There is one regional mux and one national but plans are for more local transmitters. Austria's digital radio office sells a range of DAB receivers direct to the public.

AZERBAIJAN   A small network of DAB+ transmitters came on stream in 2019, serving up twelve stations to 3 million residents in the capital.

DAB & DAB+ The Future of Radio

BELGIUM   The Flemish part of Belgium has had DAB+ coverage since 2018 and the Walloon (French speaking) part since 2019. Population coverage of the 12 DAB+ stations DAB+ signals is now around 95%, matching the regular DAB coverage, and almost 40% of new cars have DAB+ installed. There are now almost 900,000 DAB+ receivers in use in Belgium, most are tune to the 'old style' 16 DAB services.

CZECH Republic
DAB broadcasting began in the Czech republic in 2005 after a five year experiment. There are three regional multiplexes plus one in Prague, carrying 54 stations, 20 of which are exclusively DAB. Coverage has now reached 95% and the closedown of LW and MW stations is set for 2021.

DENMARK
FM has been the main channel for radio in Denmark since the 1950s, and the state broadcaster, *Danish Radio (DR),* began DAB transmissions in 2002. Today, Denmark has two national multiplexes, both run by DR, but one of which carries some private stations as well as DR's P1 to P8. Six private stations are now available on the regional muxes.

By 2020 only around 20% of listening was on DAB, so the government have proposed to switch off FM transmitters by 2021. Take up of DAB has been slow, with only half the nine available slots on a local DAB multiplex being in use by mid 2020. About half (14) of the DAB services in Denmark are in DAB+, but ten are exclusive.

FRANCE
By 2020, DAB coverage had only reached 25% of the French population. There are fifteen regional multiplexes: six on air in Paris, four in Nice, four in Marseille and one in Lille. There are currently 166 services on the air, 90 of them are exclusively DAB+ and 76 are also on AM and FM. The regulator plans local multiplexes in more cities including Marseille, Rennes, Caen, Nancy, Paris and Bordeaux.

DAB & DAB+ The Future of Radio

New legislation now mandates the inclusion of DAB+ in all new radios sold there, for home, portable and in-car use. In addition to the state channels, 39 stations have been awarded licenses for carriage on the national networks. Launches took place in Toulouse and Bordeaux in November 2020 however, the new DAB+ services were delayed until 2021.

GERMANY
The federal parliament issued new laws governing radio in 2019, which means that all new cars (but not trucks and vans) must have a digital radio, either DAB or IP. Over 16 million DAB radios have now been sold in Germany, but penetration is still low – about 30% of households having access to a digital radio.

There are two national and 26 regional multiplexes as well as four local multiplexes, offering 266 stations across Germany's länder. Sixty seven are exclusively DAB and 195 are simulcasts. Eighty stations are commercial, the remainder are public. Germany's first national DAB+ network has over 120 transmitters reaching about 96% of all people.

GIBRALTAR
Two DAB+ ensembles have been on air since 2013 with four GBC (state) stations, simulcasting the existing FM services. They are operated by Arqiva. There are no plans currently to switch off the FM transmitters on Gibraltar.

GREECE
Greece has a national multiplex on the air run by state broadcaster the ERT, covering the capital city of Athens, as well as part of Thessaloniki in northern Greece, and part of Patras. This will eventually be expanded to use 167 sites across Greece, but economic circumstances and financial restrictions have delayed implementation of the plan. The plan divides the country into 34 regions, with each being allocated four multiplexes.

DAB & DAB+ The Future of Radio

The service currently on the air has seven ERT services broadcasting, all in DAB+. A commercial trial local DAB+ multiplex is also on air in Athens, with nine stations broadcasting on DAB+. The first private trials were made in Thessaloniki in 2018 covering central Macedonia and simulcasting some existing FM stations.

IRELAND

The republic of Ireland introduced DAB in 2006 after trials over the previous eight years. National Public Broadcaster RTÉ has been operating a full-service multiplex across a five transmitter network which reached 52% of the population in the main cities. The DAB service carried the four existing analogue stations and five new RTE services, all music based.

The RTE service was allocated Channel 12C and offered listeners eleven programmes: *RTÉ Radio 1, RTÉ Radio 1 Extra, RTÉ Radio 2, Lyric FM, Radio Na Gaeltachta, RTÉ Choice, RTÉ Gold, 2XM, RTÉ Junior, RTÉ Chill* and *RTÉ Pulse*. All were originally transmitted at 128 kbps in stereo.

A short lived trial broadcast as **Mux2** in the Dublin area in 2007 with ten programmes, including four channels from *Communicorp. Q102, Radio Kerry, Today FM* and *Spin* are some of the stations heard, but this trial was closed in mid 2008 to await a full licence. Regulators ComReg and the BCI have paused development pending changes in the regulatory framework for digital radio multiplex licensing.

 Total DAB operated a trial in the Waterford area in from 2010 for four years from sites in the Blackstairs Mountains and Waterford City which ran for two years. It was Ireland's first privately owned DAB multiplex and the first to carry any DAB+ stations. Total's DAB offered a dozen local and regional stations plus UCB Ireland.

Another trial service in Cork carried two religious stations – *Radio Maria* and *UCB* and a new channel called *Juice Cork*. Yet another trial, run by *dB Digital Broadcasting,* offered six stations in both DAB and DAB+ and broadcast to Ireland's two main cities, Dublin and Cork.

The Cork trial also carried Newcastle on Tyne based *Amazing Radio*, the first licensed UK service to broadcast terrestrially in Ireland. Total Broadcast's trial offered a mix of DAB and DAB+ simulcasts from Irish based FM stations as well as stations exclusive to DAB/DAB+.

The Broadcasting Act in Ireland also made a provision for existing commercial broadcasters in multiplex broadcasting areas to migrate to DAB, which includes an extension to their licence of up to six years. The Broadcasting Authority of Ireland has not yet addressed the issue of establishing an appropriate regulatory framework.

One Irish operator launched several unlicensed services called the FreeDAB Network. Its aims were three-fold; to widen the service offered to listeners, to help promote DAB and thirdly, to give small broadcasters a chance to access the airwaves. Multiplexes were aired in Dublin, Cork, Sligo, Waterford and Donegal. Each offered a changing spectrum of programmes, some from the UK and other countries such as *Polish Radio IRL, Dance UK, Sovereign Gold, Wild Country* and *Zenith Rock*.

The regulator ComReg mounted several raids on the unlicensed transmitters, with help from the Gardai, in early 2020 and silenced them. Three multiplexes have returned to the air however late in 2020 and can be heard with a wide variety of programmes in Dublin, Cork and Waterford.

In 2019, the RTE had announced that they would be halting their **DAB Ireland Mux 1** service due to economic problems. The closedown was set for Easter 2020, but the move was postponed and the stations are still transmitting almost a year later.

DAB & DAB+ The Future of Radio

ITALY

DAB test began in the early 2000s, and in 2009, AGCOM (the Italian Communications Authority) approved regulation which set out steps for the roll out of digital radio across Italy.

Since 2020, all radios sold in Italy must have digital reception capabilities. Around 84% of Italy's population can already receive DAB and some districts have been switching off FM stations. The *RAS (state broadcaster in the Alps, South Tirol)* is no longer investing in FM transmitters due to the higher costs. RAS has 212 sites broadcasting three main services, but its 92 DAB sites have 22 programmes, audible by 99% of the population.

The RAI (the Italian state broadcaster) has 18 sites serving about 45% of the population in the major cities of Rome, Venice, Milan, Naples and Palermo.

DAB Italia is a private operator with about fifty sites on air. They offer 8 simulcasts of FM stations plus about ten new DAB exclusive programmes. *EuroDAB Italia* serves over three quarters of the population using forty sites. They offer six simulcasts of FM stations and a further three exclusive to DAB services.

In addition to the three national networks, eight local muxes serve up to 80% of the population and are operated by *DAB Media, Digiloc, CD DAB, DBTAA* and *Vatican Radio* in Rome. In total, there are over a hundred DAB+ stations simulcasting FM services and a couple of dozen exclusively DAB+ stations.

There are approximately five million DAB radios in Italian homes and cars. Broadcast licences in Italy run for 12 years, and for multiplex operators they are for 20 years. By the end of 2020 95% of Italian highways, 84% of the country's population and 55% of Italy are covered by DAB+ services.

KUWAIT

Kuwait has state and private commercial radio. One of the leading companies is the Sultan Telcom group, which also operates FM transmitters. DAB+ transmissions began in Kuwait in 2014, using a SFN carrying 16 programmes. It gives 100% coverage of the 4 million Kuwaiti residents.

DAB & DAB+ The Future of Radio

MALTA
The regulator, the Malta Broadcasting Authority, has embraced digital radio since awarding the first DAB licenses in 2006. Licences run for eight years. *DigiB Network* operates the national multiplex, and plans to increase available services to 60 channels, with the introduction of the third Multiplex.

Malta was the first European country to roll out a DAB+ network in 2008. There are over 40 services on the two national multiplexes which cover 100% of the population with 53 services. Over 25% of Maltese radio listeners use DAB+. The MBA has authorised the retransmission of foreign radio stations on DAB, as well as the simulcasting of twelve national analogue stations. Research by the MBA in 2018 shows only 13.4% of Maltese can access a DAB+ radio.

MONACO
Monaco Média Diffusion (MMD) serves the principality on DAB+, FM, LW and MW from its transmitter sites in Monaco and France: Maritimes Alps and Alpes-de-Haute-Provence. MMD launched its first DAB+ Mux in 2014 and now broadcasts 18 radio stations.

The stations heard on DAB+ in Monaco are: *Radio Monaco, RMC 1, MC 2, Riviera Radio, Radio Ethic, Rete 105, Radio Maria, Radio Latina, Virgin Radio, Medi 1, Ado FM, Crooner Radio, Radio Baïkal, MC Douliya, Radio Orient, Pure Radio, Fréquence Mistral, Radio Pitchoun* and *Radio Vallée* – 7 of those are exclusively on DAB+.

NETHERLANDS
The Netherlands switched off its high power medium wave transmitters recently and has re-assigned the frequencies to small low power transmitters to small area stations. A mixture of public and private stations are licenced on FM with high power allocations being auctioned. Licences are only renewed when an undertaking to transmit on DAB is made; all the national FM stations now use DAB+.

The Netherlands has two national multiplexes giving good indoor coverage across 99% of the country. One national mux is for the NPO (public broadcasters) and one for VCR (private commercial stations). Radio stations may choose to use DAB, DAB+ or DMB. Most stations have chosen to broadcast the DAB+ system.

There are almost 100 stations simulcasting FM stations, and 19 radio stations are heard exclusively on DAB. Of the public stations, 4 are simulcast while 7 are DAB+ only. There are nine private stations simulcasting and nine of those are DAB+ only.

In 2020, the Netherlands began planning a second national commercial multiplex which will be auctioned during 2021. Stations carried on the new second national multiplex will only be allowed to broadcast if they use DAB+. These licences which run for twelve years are being offered at auction with a starting bid being 50,000 Euros.

In addition to the national multiplexes, the Netherlands has 44 regional muxes – about a third of these are public and 31 are commercial. Approximately 2.5 million DAB radios have been sold in the Netherlands since 2013.

NORWAY

In 2017, Norway became the first country to completely switch off national FM services, completing a year-long process of switching off region by region. After the DSO, there was a marked decline in radio listening as receiver penetration was not complete.

The latest Nielsen Report on radio ownership says that more than 3.4 million people (almost 75% of those aged 10+) have a DAB radio in their home, which includes analogue receivers with a DAB adaptor. All new cars have DAB+ fitted as standard, due to the EECC directive.

Coverage for DAB+ is 99.7% for the NRK's (public) and 92.8 percent for commercial national service. Smaller local radio stations may broadcast on FM until 31 December 2021. Norway has a national multiplex, plus seven regional and seven local muxes. 23 stations are available nationwide – 14 public and nine are commercial. Oslo is the best served with 18 channels on the local mux, as well as the national services. All stations now transmit in DAB+ and there is no 'original' DAB transmissions still operating.

DAB & DAB+ The Future of Radio

POLAND
Regular DAB was launched by *Polskie Radio* in major cities in winter 2013. More transmitters brought coverage to 54%. Polish radio stations discussed the transition to DAB+ in May 2018 at a conference to discuss the radio's future. In 2019 KRRiT (National Broadcasting Council) announced an auction for regional and local licences for DAB+ multiplexes in 34 cities. Eleven new and extensions to 24 existing licenses were granted by FRRiT and more are to follow.

There are 27 regional multiplexes and 6 local trials taking place, offering listeners about 30 stations, mostly simulcasts from AM and FM but a few are heard exclusively on DAB.

PORTUGAL
Portugal has decided to abandon its DAB network; see their entry in the following section on DAB switch off, see page 57.

SLOVENIA
DAB+ was launched in 2016, on the first R1 national network, operated by public broadcaster RTV Slovenia. It was filled by 2019 and a second national multiplex to be available, with stations using DAB+ only, was launched in Autumn 2020. The first R1 network carries 19 stations and reaches 85% of Slovene homes. A new R3 network is based in Ljubljana.and all three networks are operated by RTV Slovenia.

SOUTH KOREA
The Korean government's KCC (Ministry of Communication Committee) has set up a research project to recommend a suitable standard for digital radio.
An interactive mobile TV service, or Smart DMB, launched in 2011 with six terrestrial-DMB operators (T-DMB). With Smart DMB, mobile TV viewers are able to search the internet, receive EPG information updates, and enjoy 'TV Screen Capture and Share Service' while watching television. 13 new nationwide licences were granted for DMB services. There are also two audio only services carried on the DMB networks.

SPAIN

The *Spanish DAB Association* comprising both national private and public broadcasters is responsible for DAB/DAB+ regulation in Spain. National station licenses are issued by the central government, while local and regional licenses are the responsibility of the regional government. Radio licenses are valid for 10 years with automatic renewal for a further 10 years and operators must commit to the promotion of DAB digital radio.

Three types of DAB service have been authorised in Spain: National (3), Regional and Local (237). The only DAB services on the air are in Madrid and in Barcelona, reaching about 20% of the population. Nineteen stations can be found on the multiplexes, all are old style DAB and only one transmits in DAB+

SWEDEN

DAB transmissions in Sweden started in 1995 and today population coverage stands at 42%, with services from public service broadcaster Swedish Radio (SR) and commercial radio.

The Swedish Broadcasting Authority (*Teracom*) awarded licences for 25 commercial radio stations in 2014; 21 were for national coverage and four for regional coverage. There are now over 50 stations on the air, about half are exclusively DAB+ services.

Swedish Radio operates a DAB multiplex (Mux 1) which covers 42% of the population and has six services. SR has one national and four regional multiplexes. The MUX 2 carries 14 channels, all are DAB+. It covers Stockholm, Uppsala, Gävle. Gothenburg and Malmö, which comprise 43% of the population.

Bauer Media announced the launch of DAB+ services in 2020, with multiplexes in Stockholm, Gothenburg and Malmö. Each will carry up to ten stations and reach 50% of the population by mid 2021. Public broadcaster *Swedish Radio* has requested a nationwide permit for ten channels on a new DAB+ national multiplex.

DAB & DAB+ The Future of Radio

SWITZERLAND

At the Swiss Radio Day in 2020, it was announced that "owing to positive signs from the market and to the trend in listener numbers, the radio industry plans to deactivate FM services."

The plan is that the state broadcaster SRG will switch off FM transmitters in August 2022, making it viable for commercial operators to also switch over. Private radio stations will then switch off their FM transmitters in January 2023. In order to facilitate the switch to DAB+, the Swiss media regulator announced that the financial support offered to broadcasters will increase.

In Switzerland, *Swisscom Broadcast* manage the transmitters, but the SRG is responsible for the planning of the network and multiplexing. All stations use DAB+, since 2016. There are four National muxes, three regional muxes and two local muxes, four being by the SRG. The first commercial DAB+ network launched in 2009 and has 14 stations for the German part of Switzerland. The two local muxes offer DAB+ in Geneva and in Zurich.

DAB+ reaches over 99% of the Swiss population and 99% of the roads are covered, including highway tunnels. There are 136 stations now heard on DAB, over a third of them are exclusively on digital. Digital radio usage in Switzerland is now 68%, with DAB+ the most widely used radio reception platform.

TUNISIA

Following successful trials starting in 2008, a national multiplex operated by the *Office National de la Télédiffusion* (ONT), the national public broadcaster in Tunisia, now covers 75% of Tunisia's 11 million inhabitants. The multiplex, which hosts 18 DAB+ stations, covers Tunis and north-east Tunisia.

VATICAN

The Holy See has its own DAB multiplex carrying seven services, including *Radio Vaticana, RV Euro, Radio Natale* and its two Italian services. Vatican Radio is about to celebrate its 90th birthday and recently declared that it sees digital radio as being the future of radio.

DAB & DAB+ The Future of Radio

Potential Future DAB countries?

The following countries have run trials of DAB, or have legislation in place but, so far, no licences have been issued and no stations are broadcasting in these countries

Algeria	Vietnam
Belarus	Myanmar
Brunei	New Zealand
Bulgaria	North Macedonia
China	Oman
Taipei	Qatar
Croatia	Romania
Estonia	Saudi Arabia
Indonesia	Serbia
Israel	Slovakia
Luxembourg	South Africa
Malaysia	Thailand
Mongolia	United Arab Emirates

The penetration of DAB services and the rate of adoption has varied tremendously between different regions, due to economic circumstances in each market, the historical development of radio (whether state or private networks).

DAB & DAB+ The Future of Radio

DAB SWITCH OFF

While the radio industry is still promoting the expansion of DAB in some countries, others have not found it to be the ideal medium and some large important countries have now switched off DAB or are in the process of doing so.

Some of these suspensions of DAB have been the result of some political positioning by broadcasters, seeking to expand their empire and funding and some are genuinely trying to make financial economies.

CANADA
The CBC commended building a network of L Band transmitters, however these were found to be useful only in heavily built up urban areas. Even there, the L Band signals were simply too short wavelength to be able to penetrate among the buildings very well. There were very few L-Band radios available, so Canada abandoned the campaign and one to switch off analogue radio transmissions. Canada has recently adopted the HD Radio system, as used across the border in the USA.

IRELAND
DAB transmissions to the Republic of Ireland began at the end of 2006 and coverage reached just over 50% of the population. Coverage of the RTE services however was to over 99% of the population by DVB and satellite, as well as FM and Long Wave and this has been claimed to have held up the use of DAB by the public. Even several new digital only channels did not lure listeners. The country's multiplex and the new RTE digital stations were closed as a cost-cutting measure.

Some smaller scale networks were launched by private operators *Total Broadcast Consultants* and *Viamux*, but these have now also closed. A second Irish multiplex (Mux 2) has now also closed down. Since the closures unlicensed DAB transmissions have taken place in Dublin and in Cork, however raids by *ComReg* officials and the Gardai have seen their being silenced too.

FINLAND

The state broadcaster, YLE, began with DAB in 1997. It built a complete new infrastructure of transmitters for several new services, including talk, a new classical music channel and two foreign language services called YLE World and YLE Mondo. The country's commercial sector however showed no enthusiasm to participate at all. This influenced the public's perception and regard for DAB. The YLE closed down its DAB transmitters in 2005 but the YLE has retained its transmission facilities, just in case international trends suggest that DAB is going to really take off.

PORTUGAL

The part-state and part-private radio networks were unable to persuade listeners to buy DAB radios in any significant quantities and the transmitters were switched off in 2005.

NEW ZEALAND

After a lengthy trial period, with a network of eight transmitters, New Zealand suspended DAB transmissions in 2018.

TAIWAN.

Despite being home to several leading manufacturers, including SANGEAN Taiwan decided to end its DAB trials in 2016. Commercial operator *SuperFM* set up a network in Band III that covered the major conurbations and around 5 million residents. Very few receivers were sold. A production run of 20,000 radios from one manufacturer were later dumped on the markets in Europe at 'knock down prices'.

HONG KONG.

DAB broadcasting began in Hong Kong in 2011, but after the public showed little interest in it, the three commercial broadcasters, Phoenix Radio, Digital Broadcasting Cor and Metro Radio returned their DAB licenses to the government in 2016. A few months after the state broadcaster, *Radio Hong Kong* decided there was no point in continuing and closed down the five DAB services it had been transmitting.

DAB & DAB+ The Future of Radio

DAB MYTHS

"DAB offers CD quality sound.
"DAB radio provides a crisp, clear sound".
This is a somewhat specious claim, often made by pushy salesmen but also by those in the radio industry who really should know better. The claim that "there's no hiss or crackle with DAB", is also simply misleading.

The fact is, that ALL digital radio signals drop out completely in the face of interference, leaving either a sudden silence or an annoying burbling sound instead. While analogue radio deteriorates with interference, some reception is usually still possible. This enables listeners outside normal reception areas to still hear a station, perhaps with reduced fidelity.

"DAB is easier to tune".
With increasing numbers of DAB stations, it is becoming more difficult to find the station the listener is seeking. The DAB circuitry stops at each station in turn which can take some time to scroll right through the band. One answer is to have 'wanted' stations available on pre-set buttons but this can be done too on analogue radios and is not a DAB virtue. It has been a common feature on car radios for about fifty years now; the motor industry in the UK did radio a huge disservice by failing to advise listeners how to set these buttons to stations.

The big advantage of DAB, which the salesmen rarely tell buyers, is that DAB stations are identified on screen by their name, so there is no need to remember the frequencies of radio stations. Of course, ever since the 1930s, radio dials have had station names marked on them to make it easier to tune in stations.

DAB Myths, continued

"DAB Offers more stations."

It is true that DAB is capable of carrying more stations, but the systems has been (and continues to be) strangled by over-regulation, and the policy of many regulators has been to concentrate ownership into fewer and fewer hands.

In the UK and in Ireland, this has resulted in less choice for the listener – so is it true that "the FM bandwidth can only accommodate a handful of stations without the signals overlapping."

It's really the regulators and other gatekeepers who have stifled FM. Listeners in most urban areas can hear several dozen stations, with the potential with good planning being between 70 and 150 in any area. The problem has been the traditional empire building, a reluctance to change standards and the obstinate refusal to allow new entrants into the medium.

"All radios now have DAB"
"No one makes AM or FM radios any longer"

It's a blatant lie; millions of new AM and FM radios are sold every year and dozens of manufacturers still produce them.

"FM on its way out"

In fact, FM continues to grow and ever higher prices are being paid to buy FM stations. In recent years, three companies have bought up most of the FM stations throughout the UK at very high multiples of their earnings.

Radio industry monopolists have been campaigning for a switch off of AM and FM for over a decade, but in 2020, the Government have confirmed that this will not happen before at least 2032. OFCOM have now scheduled renewals for all AM and FM stations that want them.

DAB RECEIVERS

History of receivers   (from crystal set to smartphone)
The first radio receivers were all home-made, and cobbled together from surplus military equipment, or even hand-made components such as coils and capacitors. Receivers were invariably very simple concoctions, using a crystal detector, a coil and headphones, all known as a radio 'set'. They were connected to large aerial array of wire as an antenna, strung out along the garden or, in a suburban home, perhaps festooned around a picture rail.

The crystal detector was often known as a 'cats whisker' as it was a small wire touching a small piece of a crystalline material such as galena. It rectified and demodulated the radio signal leaving only the audio modulation, which could drive a small headphone.

"Listening in" as it was called needed a pair of high impedance headphones camped onto the head. This was because the signals produced were so weak and one needed to exclude any extraneous noise. The demodulated signal was not powerful enough to drive a loudspeaker.

Valves were a real 'game changer' and meant that the whole family (often neighbours too!) could gather around the radio and listen to the far-away voices and sounds; radio really was a technological marvel.

DAB & DAB+ The Future of Radio

The first in car radios were developed by Leonard Plugge, a real radio pioneer who bought airtime on foreign stations and broadcast English language programmes with commercials. He built a radio and a loop antenna into his car and toured Europe signing new stations. Commercial radio was not allowed in the UK, the GPO refused to give a licence for it, so stations beamed programmes into Britain from other European countries.

Portable radios began to appear in the early 1930s too, using miniature valves but these were power hungry, expensive and the preserve of the rich.

The next landmark in radio receivers was a 1947 invention, the transistor. These small devices were semi-conductors that rectified and amplified signals, replacing the bulky and power-hungry valves. The transistor made it possible to have a truly portable radio, whose bulk was governed by the size of the loudspeaker and the battery. There were 18  manufacturers in the UK alone, each competing for sales.

The transistor set (as adults called it) revolutionised listening as it made radio more personal, freeing listeners from the huge valve set in the home. Teenagers finally had their own device for music and, in the USA, the personal transistor radio was a status symbol. This wasn't the case so much in the UK where radio was rigidly controlled and in the hands of the BBC. Its output was very staid and not particularly popular, but teenagers could listen to stations like Radio Luxembourg, Audible only after dark, it played the latest hits.

A huge development of the sixties was the 'Compact Cassette' recorder, which was soon joined to a radio to make the 1970's icon, the **radio-cassette recorder.** Now the listeners were able to record direct from the radio,  which invariably meant recording the Top 20 hits countdown shows, when the hits were played one after another. Fingers really worked overtime on the 'pause' button to remove the DJ dialogue!

The cassette player soon replaced a failed piece of consumer technology found mainly in cars – the 8 track cartridge player. These never took off in the UK due to their cost, but by the end of the decade cassette players were becoming ubiquitous.

The radio receiver's next development was the integrated circuit, commonly referred to as 'chips'. They were simply arrays of transistors on a single slice of semi-conductor (the chip) making it possible to put the various stages of a radio onto one component. This greatly reduced the size of radios and other electronic circuit. A problem with this incessant drive to miniaturisation that ceramic filters were used, causing poorer sound quality of AM signals.

Miniaturisation also meant that thousands and then millions of circuits could be accommodated in domestic equipment and that digital circuitry could be mass produced, enabling huge efficiencies. Digitising electronic signals has enabled digital audio, images (both still photography and video) and data transmission. Miniaturisation and cost efficiencies have combined to revolutionise all manner of communications   and entertainment, as evidenced by todays smartphones which contain billions of circuits, capable of doing almost anything.

Ignoring the many features of smartphones, even regular radios today have a wealth of features, most of which would have been impossible just a few decades ago.

DAB & DAB+ The Future of Radio

While the BBC began transmitting DAB in the mid 1990s, radio manufacturers were reluctant to mass produce sets, which had several inherent faults – not the least of which was the large power consumption and lack of popular programming. The only receivers cost hundreds of pounds and were of very limited appeal.T his was eventually overcome by the duplication of commercial stations on DAB, circuit improvements and the lowering of prices.

The major manufacturers who are producing DAB equipped receivers today are:

Panasonic	4
Revo	15
Pure	22
Como Audio	13
VQ	41
Geneva	8
Roberts	29

At the beginning of 2020, there were over 140 different models of receivers available with DAB, over 90% of them have DAB+ capability. Many of them have other bands too; invariably FM and 40 of them have Medium Wave too. In fact, eleven have the Long Wave band and six offer short wave reception too.

Most of the personal radios are priced at up to £50, although there are some up to £100 each. Most of the table-top receivers and other mains driven radios have both DAB and DAB+ available; they cost from £70 up to over £2,300 (Ruark's flagship R7, first on sale in 2015).

There are now many models of radio which offer both DAB, and DAB+ as well as an online section too, enabling the listener to tune into many tens of thousands of stations from around the world.

To list each model and give a fair review of it is beyond the scope of this book, but the *Radio Listener Guide*, an annual publication, and in its 156 pages their experts David Harris and Phil Wright review all the new models fairly; a publication we recommend.

https://radioguide.co.uk

DAB RADIO FEATURES

Every DAB radio requires electrical <u>power</u> to run and the complex circuits mean that a considerable drain on the power supply is made. This means that 'dry cell' batteries are quickly exhausted on portables, so the most popular DAB radios are those which permit operation from the mains, or from a car's supply, or have rechargeable batteries installed.

Other features of DAB radios which buyers can find on radios on sale now include:

REMOTE –
usually the remote control of a DAB receiver is effected by using a small handset which allows the listener to vary the volume and change channels. This can be important if a DAB is to be located in a 'good reception' spot often in a high up (off the ground) room.

ALARM
Bedside radio alarms became popular in the late 1960s and a listener's choice is often the station they are going to be woken up by and sent to work. It's one of the reasons that the peak hours for listening to the radio are breakfast time, and many stations have their peak listening hours at that time.

SCREEN
One of DAB's advantages over traditional radio is that it offers an ability to carry other information, which is often best portrayed on a screen. As well as the station identification, its type, the time and perhaps a scrolling message giving details of the programme, a screen on a DAB may also have information or logos about commercials being played, and even artwork from the artist whose music is being aired. Screen content can also be in several colours.

DAB AERIALS

The practice by some manufacturers to use a short or hidden antenna in a portable radio, plus relatively strong signals giving decent reception, convinces some listeners that they don't really need an aerial to listen. In fact, EVERY radio needs some sort of an aerial to hear any radio station; it's simply that manufacturers can hide them inside the radio that perpetuates the illusion that there is no aerial, or antenna.

DAB needs a stronger signal than most to function, although the shorter wavelengths mean that a shorter antenna can be used, than with FM. Using an outside antenna will drastically improve DAB reception, especially for L Band, but for Band III as well. A simple folded dipole a few metres off the ground and in the clear" will make a big difference.

The basic design of aerials hasn't changed much for most of radio's life. In the very early days (the 1920s and 30) a long aerial was needed to receive signals and a simple long wire was tied up and strung down a garden.

As radio moved up in frequency to the VHF band, a good aerial could be just a few feet long – often a simple dipole was effective and if it was properly cut to the right length, this would closely match a coaxial feed cable, which would eliminate interference.

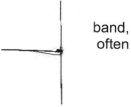

Regular dipole

Folding a simple dipole over to construct the classic 'folded dipole' gives extra bandwidth, with signals over a wider range of frequencies. This gave the receiver the best signal, in terms of both strength and quality.

Folded Dipole

DAB & DAB+ The Future of Radio

Directional antenna

Directivity can be added by placing extra elements before (directors) or behind (reflectors) the antenna which squeezes its pattern (the shape of maximum pick up) to favour one direction, or to 'play deaf' or suppress signals from an unwanted direction.

Older readers may recognise this from the old style 405 line TV antenna. Today's DAB signals use the same frequencies that were used by ITV from 1955 to the 1980s and the aerials are the same style and size.

In a vehicle, its essential to attach an antenna (aerial) as the radio is usually set inside a steel box, inside the dashboard, where it is unable to see any signal at all. It needs to collect the radio signal outside and an antenna are its 'ears'.

Vehicle roof mount

The best solution is to mount the aerial onto the car body's exterior – roof mounted is ideal as this extra elevation picks up a stronger signal, especially in weak signal areas. It's important that it is properly connected to the receiver with screened feeder. Many antennas will contain a coil; to match the signal better and perhaps an amplifier inside the base.

Screen Mounted DAB antenna

If the antenna cannot be mounted on a vehicle's roof, it can be stuck on the inside of the screen. It may have an amplifier inside a small connector box immediately adjacent to the antenna element.

Some of the antennas mounted on screens with tape do not perform well and suffer from interference, often due to electrical heating elements that have been embedded in the screen.

DAB & DAB+ The Future of Radio

DAB in cars. EU directive

Implementation of the

European Electronic Communications Code (EECC)

The European Union introduced a directive called the European Electronic Communications Code that makes it mandatory to install a digital radio receiver in every new car; this has come into effect in most countries, although the terms of the regulations mean that different standards can be adopted by countries – purchasers should not imagine that the car radio installed should have DAB and DAB+ availability. The regulation only applies to new cars.

June 2020, the UK's Department for Transport published a consultation on their proposal to mandate the fitment of terrestrial digital radio in new cars as part of their implementation of the EU Electronic Communications Code.

In August 2020 the necessary legal regulations were approved by Parliament to support the mandating of the fitment of digital radio in passenger vehicles in the UK. The new order, which came into force in 2020, is in line with the EU's EECC directive, which mandates digital radio in new cars across Europe.

Before the CoVid 19 pandemic, there were almost 41 million cars, vans, trucks and buses on the road in the UK (DVLA road tax figures) and its estimated that over 40m are equipped with a radio receiver.

DAB & DAB+ The Future of Radio

PENETRATION of DAB

The penetration of DAB equipped radios varies considerably, depending on various factors: the availability of popular programmes, the weight of the campaign to persuade listeners to buy DAB Radios, and of course the price of the radios. The first receivers, in the mid 1990s, had a hefty price tag of around £1,000.

Even today, a factory fitted DAB radio in a luxury car will be priced at over £1000, although it is likely to have several other extra services, such as a terrestrial TV tuner (Freeview) and a screen, Satellite Navigation, and video of a rear-facing camera. Some still have LW and MW, although the AM band is being found on less and less radios, but FM is still prevalent.

The following are the estimated sales totals of DAB (and DAB+) radios in selected countries which have made the sales information available:

COUNTRY	DAB RADIOS SOLD (m)	POPULATION COVERED
UK	45	97%
Germany	16.6	98%
Norway	7	99.7%
Australia	6	64%
Italy	5.3	84%
Switzerland	5.1	99.5
France	3.4	25%
Netherlands	2.2	95%
Denmark	1.3	99.9
Belgium	1.2	97%

The information for the table on the previous page was provided by WorldDAB, its members and partners, including market research agencies, broadcasters, national digital radio bodies, ministries and governments. WorldDAB collates data on DAB and publishes it on its website: www.*worlddab.org*.

DAB+ is now the usual system used at the launch of new DAB services, and is in use in, among other places, Australia, Norway, Switzerland, Belgium, Germany, The Netherlands, and many more. The main benefit from using the DAB+ systems is that the multiplex operator can get many more channels onto a typical DAB multiplex.

UK RADIO Listening

THE UK is one of the biggest DAB markets with over 68 million inhabitants, around 97% of whom are within the coverage area of at least one DAB network.   There are a little under 500 stations using DAB to reach listeners. The car market is particularly important, with over 94% of new vehicles having a DAB radio, although the majority of cars "on the road" are very old and do not have DAB fitted as standard – offering huge potential for the 'after sales' market.

In the UK, 40% of DAB listening is now DAB+ *(Q1 2020)*

DAB+ listening
By the end of 2020, around half of the UK's national commercial radio stations were using the newer DAB+. Four years previously, the first stations to use DAB+ in the UK had been Jazz FM and Magic chilled, each being niche format stations which the operators could not justify the enormous cost of regular DAB coverage on the big transmitters. Since then more commercial stations launched using DAB+, some of them are only available on DAB+. The BBC still uses the original DAB format for its stations.

Some receivers (mainly made by PURE) cannot be upgraded from DAB only to receive the new DAB+ transmissions. Pure offer a software upgrade on their web site to enable listeners to upgrade their radios.

DAB & DAB+ The Future of Radio

Add-on adapters have become popular among car owners to enable traditional car radios to receive DAB signals. Some of the after-market radio manufacturers are now selling units that include DAB and DAB+, online radio and streams (such as Spotify) and SatNav into one unit, along with control of rear-facing cameras, dash-cams, DVD playout and off-air TV distribution. These operate using Android or Apple's CarPlay operating systems and sell for between $150 and $800. They have a variety of screen sizes, up to 10 inches, and require a 2-DIN aperture for installation

DAB+ is now the standard way to launch new DAB services, and is in use in, among other places, Australia, Norway, Switzerland, Belgium, Germany, The Netherlands, and many more. The main benefit is that you can get many more channels onto a typical DAB multiplex.

digitalradio ☑

DAB+ Tick Mark
A symbol to signify that a radio is capable of receiving the newer DAB+ stations is a large green tick, seen in advertising and often as a sticker on the receiver itself.

The Digital Radio "Tick Mark" identifies that the DAB products are future-ready and will enable them to receive the available DAB, DAB+ and FM radio stations. In order to be granted use of the Tick Mark, manufacturers must meet the minimum specification. In order for the manufacturer to prove that they meet the minimum specification, they must put their product(s) (or installation services) through a testing process.

DAB & DAB+ The Future of Radio

DAB Radio Products

Many radios built to pick up the original DAB transmissions cannot resolve DAB+ transmissions. This is as many as the first five million DAB radios sold in the UK; some are unable to tune low enough to hear the multiplexes in blocks 7 and 8, and some don't have the circuitry needed to decode the DAB+ audio.

The following products are the main types that should decode DAB+ and are eligible for the *Digital Tick Mark:*

> DAB receivers (domestic and in-vehicle)
> HIFI units with DAB (domestic)
> DAB head units (in-vehicle)
> DAB adapters (in-vehicle and domestic)
> New vehicles (in-vehicle)

DIGITAL RADIO SWITCHOVER

The UK radio industry is committed to a digital future for radio and is working towards a Digital Radio Switchover in which ALL analogue stations will be switched off, at any cost. This has been staunchly resisted by many, particularly listeners and those who don't have a vested interest in the expansion of DAB, as it would instantly make all non-DAB radio receivers redundant. There are estimated to be over 100 million non-DAB radios in the UK.

The Government decided to delay taking such a huge, irreversible and potentially damaging step. The DCMS set the following criteria for setting a date for switchover:

- Digital listening share to reach 50%. This has been met, if one includes listening to online and TV carried digital radio.

- When local commercial and national DAB coverage reaches FM equivalence. (now met)

UK DAB STATIONS

The first organisation to transmit DAB in the UK was the BBC. They have since expanded their national DAB network to over 400 transmitter sites and now achieve coverage of 97% of the UK's population.

The main eleven BBC radio services are carried on the Corporation's own **BBC NATIONAL** mux, which is all DAB, with no DAB+ services. Some BBC services are carried on the commercially-run multiplexes, local and regional.

The commercial sector was cajoled into taking part in DAB by the regulator offering automatic licence extensions, i.e. without any competing bids being considered. The local and regional ensembles cover 77.8% of UK households.

Digital One was the UK's first commercial multiplex, operated by Arqiva. The Digital One network launched in November 1999 and has held the only digital radio licence for national commercial radio in the UK ever since. A new company, **SDL National** transmits a mixture of DAB and DAB+ stations, including *TALK, VIRGIN* & *Times Radio.*

BBC NATIONAL multiplex

The BBC is currently broadcasting the following services on its national digital radio multiplex:

BBC Radio 1

Previously a Top 40 oriented station "aimed at the young and young at heart", Radio 1 was once the UK's most listened to station. Its mission now – only new music & issues.

Radio 1Xtra

Radio 1Xtra focuses on all shades and genres of black music and culture including Hip Hop, R'n'B, Drum & Bass and Dancehall.

BBC Radio 2

The station originally established to replace the BBC programme, melodious and gentle music for the older listeners. It has since dropped most genres of music and its 'older and more relaxed' appeal. It has become a Radio 1 and a quarter, focussed on the more commercial modern music. Radio 2 is the most listened to radio station in the UK.

BBC Radio 3

Serious music (Classical, jazz and world music) plus high-brow lectures, drama and discussion about The Arts. Its output also covers Opera, World Music, and other niche genres. The BBC describes Radio 3 as "the world's most significant commissioner of new music." The station's *New Generation Artists scheme* funds and promotes young musicians.

BBC Radio 4

The BBC brands its Radio 4 channel as "the home of intelligent speech radio". It carries deep discussions, lengthy news and several 'issues-based' magazine programmes, with lengthy dramas.

BBC 4 Extra

Radio 4's *extra* channel carries many repeats of old programmes, mainly classic comedy, drama and features.

BBC Radio 5

A rolling service of live news, chat and sport, with commentaries of major football games, presented mostly in an upbeat style, aimed at younger listeners.

5 Live Sports Extra

Five Live Sports Extra offers coverage of sporting events not scheduled elsewhere on its main Radio 5 Live network.

BBC 6 Music

A mixture of contemporary and classic artists, plus new talent, drawing on the BBC's archive material. The music heard on Radio Six is usually adult-oriented with an emphasis on albums rather than singles.

Asian Network

The Adsan Network broadcasts a mix of contemporary speech (news and issues) and music of appeal to British Asians.

World Service

The BBC's international radio station; for many years it was a called the Empire Service, and a 'shop window' for all things British and a link to the mother country for ex-patriates and Anglophiles. The World Services has now become predominantly a stream of news and discussions of and issues from around the world linked by mainly non-English voices.

Coverage

The BBC's National multiplex, carrying eleven BBC national radio stations, covers most of the United Kingdom and can be tuned to be over 97% of the population. It uses the legacy DAB system with high bitrates

Other BBC services

In addition to the BBC's own national network, about fifty of its services are also carried on the regional and local DAB muxes, operated by commercial companies. This includes the national services for Wales, Scotland and Northern Ireland and those countries' language serves as well as pop ups, etc. The BBC's forty local stations in English counties are also carried on the relevant local commercial DAB multiplexes.

(see pages 83 and 84 below, after the national commercial services)

SOUND DIGITAL ONE
(1st national commercial multiplex)

Digital One was launched as the UK's only national commercial DAB network in 1999, by the GWR Group and NTL, a management buy-out of the old IBA engineering division. The original licence was to carry ten stations, including the three INR licensees: **Classic FM, Virgin and TalkRadio.** The other channels were to be *Planet Rock, Club Dance, OneWord* (comedy & drama), *Capital Life* (Soft AC format targeting females), a sports channel and *CORE* (a Top 40 and dance music station). Some were scrapped before the multiplex launched.

In 2004, NTL sold its transmitters to a subsidiary of the Maquarie Group, which became ARQIVA, who bought the GWR stake in Digital One from Capital Radio in 2008. Capitals two channels on Digital one were closed when they sold out to Global later in 2008.

Digital One now use 160 transmitters, reaching 90% of the country's households. It is still run by Arqiva, who operate all the television and most radio transmitters in the UK.

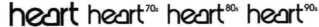

DAB & DAB+ The Future of Radio

The stations currently carried on **Digital One** are:

Absolute Radio - *Bauer* – Adult alternative music

Heart 70s - *Global* – Music from the 1970s

Heart 80s - *Global* – Music from the 1980s

Heart 90s - *Global* – Music from the 1990s

Capital XTRA - *Global* – Urban and dance music

Classic FM - *Global* – Classical music

Heart UK - *Global* – Adult contemporary music

Kiss UK - *Bauer* – Hip-hop, R&B, urban & dance

LBC - *Global* – News and Talk service.

LBC News - *Global* – Speech

Magic - *Bauer* – Soft adult contemporary music

Radio X - *Global* – Rock music

Smooth UK - *Global* – Melodic hits

TalkSPORT - Wireless Group – Sport and talk

Capital - *Global* – Contemporary hit music

Gold - *Global* – well-known hits of the last 25 years

UCB 1 - *United Christian Broadcasters* – Christian music

Kisstory – *Bauer* - hip-hop, R&B, urban & dance

Heart Dance - *Global* – Dance classics

Capital XTRA Reloaded - *Global* – hip-hop

SOUND DIGITAL
(2nd national commercial multiplex)

The second network, SDL, is called a semi-national system and it reaches around 83% of the population, offering an optimum combination of national coverage and cost-efficiencies. Arqiva provide the 45 transmitter sites facilities in association with Bauer and the Wireless Group.

The Sound Digital network is the first national network to offer some stations with the newer DAB+ technology for some of the services. DAB+ uses less bandwidth than the original DAB service, allowing Sound Digital to carry more stations, this expanding listener choice. IA further 19 transmitters are being added, to reach an extra 1.6m listeners.

Nine of the networks stations use the DAB+ technology, with bit rates of either 24 or 32 kilobits per second. The other 13 transmit in the original DAB format with higher bit rates (up to 112 kbit/s), all bar one programme are in mono.

SD's 18 national radio stations including three DAB+ services were the biggest commercial radio launch ever, with the network at 98% capacity. This has now been increased by using lower bit rates.
SOUND DIGITAL

DAB & DAB+ The Future of Radio

The stations now carried on **Sound Digital** are:

TalkRADIO - *Wireless Group* - News and current affairs
TalkSPORT 2 - *Wireless Group* - Live sports and sports talk
Times Radio   *Wireless Group* - News and Culture
Virgin Radio - *Wireless Group* - Rock and pop music
Virgin Chilled - *Wireless Group* - laid back rock
Virgin Anthems - *Wireless Group* - rock and alternative hits
Mellow Magic - *Bauer* - Relaxing and melodic music
Absolute 80s - *Bauer* - 80s music
Absolute 90s - *Bauer* - 90s music
Planet Rock - *Bauer* - Classic rock music
Scala Radio - *Bauer* - Light and Classical music
Sunrise Radio – *Sunrise* - Asian music and speech
UCB 2 - *United Christian Broadcasters* - Christian music
Premier Christian Radio – *Premier* - Christian music
Premier Praise - Premier Media - Popular Christian music
Love Sport Radio - A Spokesman Said Ltd - Sports talk.
Fun Kids - *Folder Media* - National children's radio station
BFBS – *SSVC* Entertainment and news service
Jazz FM - *Jazz FM* - Jazz, blues and soul
Jack Radio – *Jack FM* – all female music
Union Jack – *Jack FM* – all British music

*Union Jack are reorganising their
channels into rock and dance formats.*

REGIONAL AND LOCAL MUXES

The regional and local muxes for each area are operated by one of the following companies:

Bauer	Bauer Digital Radio Ltd
C.E.	C.E. Digital Limited. (Bauer)
DRG	Digital Radio Group. (Global)
MUXCO	Folder Media JV with Arqiva
NOW.	Now Digital (Arqiva)
SWITCH	Switch Digital, The Wireless Group

The **REGIONAL** and the **LOCAL** multiplexes are all mandated to carry the relevant local and regional BBC services as well as commercial radio stations. Some of them recently began to carry a limited number of DAB+ services, though most are legacy DAB transmissions only.

AREA	Sites	Operator.	Channel
Aberdeen	3	Switch	11C
Ayr	4	NOW	11B
Berks & Hants	4	NOW	12D
Birmingham		C.E.	
Bournemouth	3	NOW	11B
Bradford & Huddersfield		Switch	
Bristol	8	NOW	11B
Cambridge	1	NOW	11C
Central Scotland		Switch	
Cornwall	12	SoWest	11B
Coventry	7	NOW	12D
Derbyshire	3	NOW	10B
Edinburgh	7	Bauer	12D
Essex	6	NOW	12D
Exeter & Devon		NOW	
Glasgow	10	Bauer	11C
Gloucestershire	4	Muxco	10C
Herefordshire and Worc's	3	Muxco	12A
Herts, Beds & Bucks	9	NOW	10D
Humberside	7	Bauer	10D

DAB & DAB+ The Future of Radio

AREA	Sites	Operator.	Channel
Inverness	2	Bauer	11B
Kent	5	NOW	11C
Lancashire	4	Bauer	12A
Leeds	4	Bauer	12D
Leicestershire	6	NOW	11B
Lincolnshire	3	Muxco	12A
Liverpool	5	Bauer	10C
London 1	11	NOW	12C
London 2	24	Switch	12A
London 3	15	DRG	11B
Manchester	5	C.E.	12C
Mid &West Wales	4	Muxco	12D
NE Wales & Cheshire	3	Muxco	10D
Norfolk	5	NOW	11B
North West Wales	2	Muxco	10D /12D
North Yorkshire	4	Muxco	10C
Northamptonshire	6	NOW	10C
Northern Ireland	11	Bauer	12D
Nottingham	3	NOW	12C
Oxfordshire	5	NOW	10B
Peterborough	8	NOW	12D
Plymouth	5	SoWest	12D
Somerset	3	Muxco	10B
South East Wales	8	NOW	12C
South Hants	5	NOW	11C
South Yorkshire	6	C.E.	11C
Stoke on Trent		Switch	
Suffolk	3	Muxco	10C
Surrey	7	Muxco	10C
Sussex		Switch	
Swansea		Switch	
Swindon	3	NOW	11C
Tayside	4	Bauer	11B
Teesside	6	Bauer	11D
Tyne and Wear	12	Bauer	11C
Wiltshire	3	NOW	12D
Wolverhampton & Shropshire	2	NOW	11B

SMALL SCALE DAB

Ofcom began experimenting with small-scale DAB in 2013 to test the technology and prove its ability to allow existing small stations, as well as new services, to broadcast cost-effectively on digital radio. This new initiative was designed to open DAB to a new tier of small scale broadcasters looking to offer unique, local community focused radio stations.

Pioneered by Ofcom engineer, Rash Mustapha, the Small-Scale DAB experiment proposed using some freely available software and computer technology to transmit digital radio services and broadcast to a relatively small geographic area. It allows stations to use inexpensive equipment to transmit for far less money than had previously been possible.

EQUIPMENT
The SS DAB pioneers took advantage of the huge improvements in computing technology since DAB launched in the mid 90's. Much of the very expensive and custom designed hardware of conventional DAB transmission has been replaced by open source and freely downloadable software systems running on powerful everyday computers. It became cheap to mass produce and replicate. What had previously been £1000's or £10,000's for a studio encoder or multiplexer hardware could now be implemented on a £30 raspberry pi computer, the size of a credit card.

By 2015, a company called *Monkeyboard* offered a DAB+ FM Digital Radio development board for about £70. It provides a basis for developing DAB+ with a SlideShow and FM receiver. There was also a DAB Board from *uGreen* that turned a Raspberry Pi into a fully configurable DAB Radio and a part of a *Brainport* project in Holland enabled use of an extremely low cost board. The processing power of the Raspberry Pi proved more than ample to encode half a dozen radio stations simultaneously, the main limiting factor being the temperature of its processor.

DAB & DAB+ The Future of Radio

The Experiment

Rash built the UK's first small-scale DAB 'multiplex' in 2012 and, using an OFCOM 'Test & Development' licence, he built the UK's first small scale DAB 'multiplex' using block 10C in Band III. Rash installed the low power experimental transmitter on the roof of 'Sussex Heights,' the tallest tower block in Brighton.

**Small Scale DAB pioneer Rash Mustapha
with Radio Caroline's 50kW AM transmitter**
pic by Liam Mustapha

The transmitter was driven by cheaply-sourced equipment, rather than use the expensive 'professional' gear used by the DAB multiplexes. The programme material broadcast was simply a recording of some screeching seagulls as a 'barker' channel. There were several channels of music, provided by BBC producer and composer Kerry McCarthy, who also voiced the announcements. The signals were heard clearly throughout the city, well into the South Downs, even in tunnels.

The 'lower cost technology' experiments were carried out between September 2012 and early 2013. By the Summer, OFCOM were announcing that they had been a success and proved that good quality, well-engineered transmissions could be made from equipment that didn't cost "an arm and a leg", as had been the case previously with DAB equipment.

The small scale DAB tests proved the efficacy of the DAB+ standard, which had not previously been used in the UK. OFCOM obtained the permission from the government's DCMS to conduct experiments in several other places and licensed ten operators to operate trial multiplexes. They also offered a few dozen small radio stations the chance to broadcast on SSDAB.

The 2015 SS-DAB Trials

Over fifty applications were made to OFCOM in response to the advertisement of ten licences, most of them for single transmitters. Those first ten trial licences offered were in the following towns, in England and Scotland:

Brighton	Manchester
Portsmouth	Birmingham
Woking / Aldershot	Cambridge
Bristol	Norwich
London (SFN)	Glasgow. (SFN)

All the above SSDAB multiplexes were asked to carry at least four programmes, which had to include a mixture of commercial and community stations. Originally, the trial multiplex licences were granted for a period of nine months, then fifteen months, then for 2 years, and the trials have now been without interruption for over 5 years! By Autumn 2020, OFCOM finally advertised Round One of the "permanent" licences to replace the trials.

The SS-DAB stations used blocks from 7D to 9C, which are lower frequencies than the existing legacy DAB muxes but it's planned to licence further ones in the higher blocks.

"The trial broadcasts were intended to test and aid the development of a low-cost method of delivering digital radio services," explains engineer Alan Beech. "With a new licensing framework, the system provides small scale radio stations with an affordable route onto DAB.

The first SS DAB multiplexes came on the air in August 2015 in Portsmouth and in Brighton. Rash was involved with all of the trial stations to some extent for the first two years. Some needed support more than others. He was at the commissioning of the Brighton transmitter, which remained a pet testbed for development.

Brighton SS-DAB included several 'not-for-profit' stations, including *RadioReverb, Gaydio, Angel Radio* from Portsmouth and *PlatformB. Other stations heard are 11Disco, Atmosphere Radio, DecaDance, Metal Meyhem radio, Mi-House, Solar, Starpoint Soul,Trickstar, URF, Totally Radio and Mi-Soul.* An expansion of choice for the listener by a factor of three or four.

DAB & DAB+ The Future of Radio

Portsmouth's DAB launched on 19th August 2015 and operates under the name Solent Wireless. Its managed by Ash Elford of *Angel Radio* and the equipment was assembled and engineered by Radio Caroline engineer Alan Beech who had been one of the pioneers who worked tirelessly to develop the equipment and new circuitry.

The two mini-muxes in Brighton and Portsmouth came on the air first, with others following shortly afterwards, before the second national multiplex (SDL which launched in March 2016. All helped heighten awareness of DAB generally.

SSDAB pioneer Alan Beech
installs a fan into the Portsmouth transmitter
– 28 stations from just one box!

The *Solent Wireless* transmitter is located at Fort Widley at the top of Portdown Hill in Cosham, Portsmouth. It has an effective radiated power output of about 200 watts and the coverage is better than had been predicted. Good reception is usually possible over the greater Portsmouth area and across the Solent onto the Isle of Wight.

COSTS

A variety of software was used and evaluated in the initial experiments which were conducted by Rashid Mustapha. OFCOM carefully considered the likely cost to small scale radio station and predicted that the launch costs for an SS DAB transmitter could be only a seventh the cost of using an FM transmitter. In fact, the cost of the entire DAB multiplex carrying six or more service would be similar to the cost of one FM transmitter. This assumed a bit rate of 160, whereas using DAB+ and lower bit rates would enable each multiplex to carry even more services.

"The whole point of SSDAB is to move the goalposts away from the current gatekeepers and allow experimental and low budget stations access to the DAB airwaves," says Alan Beech, Chief `Engineer at Solent Wireless and the supply company *Commtronix* (see page 112). "The small scale muxes are designed to afford DAB access to community stations, who won't need or want 'county wide' coverage."

"SSDAB transmission costs are typically around £100-£150 per month, compared to over £2,000 on the commercial muxes, which are often operated by the big radio groups and their subsidiaries. It's been suggested that they have no incentive to allow low cost stations to compete with their "big branded" stations. The reluctance and inertia of them to introduce DAB+, meant smaller stations on commercial multiplexes could never sound as good as the "big boys". DAB+ signals at 48kbps offer good quality stereo at lower costs whereas the 64kbps mono offered by the legacy DAB muxes would make small stations sound inferior.

The small scale muxes have pioneered many developments; the Bristol SSDAB introduced a graphic slideshow, long before any of the national outlets (see Chapter 28 for more details on slideshows). Both Brighton and Portsmouth SSDABs made many innovations, which have trailblazed the way forward enabling small stations to operate efficiently.

By using DAB+ and lower bit rates, each multiplex is able to to carry even more services. DAB-only receivers have been found to have varying sensitivity (>20dB) and DAB+ requires less signal, so better coverage, all of which combine to favour the SS-DAB with better coverage at a lower cost.

DAB & DAB+ The Future of Radio

The **London** SSDAB was the first to deploy multiple transmitters on an SFN (Single Frequency Network) using open source software components.

The **Norwich** SSDAB is operated by *Future Digital*, which offers 20 stations plus pop-ups and data on a system installed by Dr. Laurence Hallett and engineer Martin Spencer of Brighton-based, *Audessence*. They too were ready to start in mid August 2015 but OFCOM had to complete tests before they were allowed to launch two weeks later.

The **Aldershot** DAB (also called Woking, the towns are close together) is run by the BFBS and the mux carries only ten stations; three BFBS locals plus Brooklands Radio, Cheesy FM, News Radio UK, Caroline and Radio Woking. Unusually, it is on channel 8A, which some older radios need a full re-scan to access.

Nation Broadcasting took over the **Glasgow** SSDAB and has big expansion plans there. They brought in a new encoding solution from *Factum Radioscape.* This improved the sound quality, while improvements at the antenna boosted the signal in the centre of Glasgow.

Since taking over the Glasgow mux in 2018, Nation Broadcasting have added even more small community stations, such as *Celtic Music*, Scotland's only Celtic music broadcaster, *Pride Radio* and *Visitor Radio*, for tourists in Scotland's largest city.

Other stations audible on the Glasgow SS-DAB have included *Nation Radio UK, Panjab Radio, Passion, The Max, Chris Country, Little Radio, London Greek Radio*, community station *Paisley FM, Radio Caroline, Angel Radio*, cultural station *Awaz FM, Podcast Radio* and *Like Radio.*

DAB & DAB+ The Future of Radio

Ash Elford

"To run a successful DAB multiplex you need a great team," says Ash Elford who is platform manager for *Nation Broadcasting* as well as being a volunteer at Portsmouth's *Angel Radio.* "Solent Wireless has been supported by Tony Smith, *Commtronix, Factum Radioscape, Open Digital Radio*, plus a lot of willing volunteers"

"The future is great for listeners," said Ash in an interview with Radio Today, the online industry magazine. "Nobody is being left behind in the digital future. Small scale DAB ensures community stations, niche formats, ethnic programmes and specialist programming are catered for."

The stations offered by the Portsmouth transmitter included their own Angel Radio, a vintage music service that originated in the area as an FM community station around 2000. They also transmitted Quentin Howard's famous 'Birdsong' channel which attracted a lot of interest when it debuted as the test transmission programme for Classic FM in 1992. The birds from Howard's garden were the UK's first famous tweeters, before social media and Twitter was thought of!

Services on the Portsmouth multiplex included **Express FM**, an existing community station carrying Pompey commentaries and Havant-based **THE FLASH**, is a former RSL and online station. It offers an alternative to pop music services with a diet of classic rock singles and albums from 1960 to 1990, featuring blues and music from local bands.

Other new services to the Portsmouth airwaves were **GAYDIO** is the world's largest LGB&T radio station. An established broadcaster with a proud history, they are now available in Portsmouth for the first time featuring a unique music mix and speech of interest to the LGB&T community. **HOT RADIO** is a station that features upbeat RnB, soul and dance music from the 1990s to the present day.

DAB & DAB+ The Future of Radio

SWINGING RADIO 60s Dedicated to nothing but the 1960s, it celebrates the days when music really did swing. Featuring presenters passionate about the decade, some quirky ideas, re-sings of the PAMS jingles used in the sixties by radio ships.

LITTLE RADIO - for small children playing their favourite songs, rhymes and speech from children's entertainers.

PASSION RADIO the best of real dance from today and the past thirty years

SKYLAB RADIO - a chill out station dedicated to music for the mind, body and soul.

TOTALLY RADIO independent music, many artistes being unsigned or new with presenters passionate about the music.

The 28 stations on the Portsmouth SSDAB

The following stations are just a selection of those who have taken part in the trial broadcasts on various mini-muxes.

CHRIS COUNTRY

A UK station that's pretty obsessed about American country music. They adore the stories, the passion, the performance and the emotion of country music, real musicians playing real instruments, singing about the real world! Chris Country can be heard on DAB in many areas including London, Manchester and Liverpool, they've got phone apps and are available on Sonos, Alexa and many other devices.

THE MAX

Radio Max are a rock-based station that launched in summer 2020. They are based in Glasgow and found online and on the SSDAB in Scotland's biggest city. 'Maximum Music / Maximum Sport / Maximum Radio' is their strapline and their mantra.

OXYGEN RADIO

Based in Bedlington, Northumberland, Oxygen provides a local radio service for the community offering music and entertainment with details of local events, local news, and activities within the area and keeping people up to date with local information about their community.

SKYLAB RADIO. Skylab Radio is a music-driven radio station playing chillout, lounge, ambient, downtempo and soft house music. Being part of the trial has also supported the introduction of specialist late night programming. Skylab is a small operation, with specialist music.

STRAWBERRY RADIO is named after 10cc's recording studio in Stockport. The station plays hits from the last five decades, as well as new music and showcasing local talent. The owner, Paul Taylor plans to use small-scale DAB to offer a local radio service for Stockport. "Small-scale DAB has enabled Strawberry Radio to take the business to the next level, from online to an 'over the air' radio station," says Paul. "We can reach a wider audience to promote not only our on-air offering, but also theatre shows and outdoor events schedule, including their own Festival."

DAB & DAB+ The Future of Radio

COSORO RADIO is an Afrobeat station based in Manchester and in Lagos, Nigeria, heard on small-scale DAB in Glasgow, Norwich & Portsmouth. Its aim is to share African music with the world and founder Femi Bankole believes that being on small-scale DAB has grown listener numbers.

BLACK CAT RADIO

Founded by long time broadcaster Tony Gillham, Black Cat is a radio station for the community, run for the community. "All you need to know and the world's greatest music." *Black Cat Radio* is a 'not-for profit' company and quickly became the 'voice' of St Neots, its home town. After winning a full time FM licence it is heard too on the DAB+mux in Cambridge.

GAYDIO

Gaydio became the UK's first LGBT FM radio service when it launched full-time in 2010. Its aimed at lesbian, gay, bisexual and transgender (LGBT) community and broadcasts on 88.4 FM in Greater Manchester, on DAB digital radio in Greater London, and on other small scale DAB muxes. It is also heard online, mobile apps and the UK Radio Player.

HCR

A community radio station serving Huntingdon since 1995, it is a not-for-profit limited company. HCR104fm won an FM licence in 2009 and is now on Cambridge's SS DAB mux.

MATRYOSHKA

This is the first Russian language radio station to win a British broadcasting licence. It's been broadcasting on DAB in London since November, 2015 and is now also carried on the Glasgow DAB and on FM in Marbella. *https://matryoshka.fm*

DAB & DAB+ The Future of Radio

ANGEL RADIO
One of the stations on the second DAB trial mux in Portsmouth, Angel Radio targeted older listeners, both to be volunteers and to listen. With lashings of nostalgia and traditional style programmes and presentation, it gained the support of several MPs and won eleven awards in its first year on the air. Angel Radio cost founder Tony Smith over £100,000 to set up but the station soon began attracting financial support from the National Lottery and other charities.

DESI RADIO
Known as 'The Sound of the Five Rivers', Desi Radio serves the Panjabi community with a colourful mix. The station discusses practices, customs and traditions to create a better understanding of the Panjabi culture. Aiming is to encourage the transformation and change in society, Desi Radio's volunteers are trained by The Panjabi Centre. The radio station was licensed in May 2002 and is now heard on one of the London Small Scale DABs.

FUN KIDS
This station is part of the Fun Kids Podcast Network, owned by Children's Radio UK Ltd, now run by Matt Deegan and Greg Watson. The concept of the radio station aimed at children was the brainchild of TV presenter, Susan Stranks who was a director.

Fun Kids is a children's media brand with two radio stations, *Fun Kids* and *Fun Kids Junior*, both heard on SS DABs with DAB+ emissions. Its programmes are designed to be educational and are presented in a responsible but entertaining manner. Fun Kids also has a well-developed website as well as video and social products and has expanded into podcasts.

SOLAR RADIO is a specialist soul music station broadcasting soul, jazz and blues. It was one of the first small scale DAB stations and had previously broadcast on satellite and online.

RADIO REVERB

Brighton's 'sound of your city' began in 2004 with a two week RSL trial broadcast and later an FM community radio licence. It's an accessible, sustainable and accountable grassroots radio station for Brighton and Hove, broadcasting topics as diverse as the arts, healthy living, business, community issues, food and drink and the environment, alongside highly regarded specialist music shows covering a range of genres.

RESONANCE

Launched in December 2015, *Resonance Extra* is dedicated to global music, sound art and radio art based at Resonance, London's community radio station for the arts. Resonance Extra broadcasts online via its website and Radioplayer as well as on ss DAB muxes in Brighton, Bristol, Cambridge, Greater London and Norwich.

They operated **Radiophrenia 2020** at the end of the year as a temporary arts radio station, a two-week exploration into current trends in sound and transmission arts. Broadcasting live from Glasgow's Centre for Contemporary Arts, the station aims to promote radio as an art form, encouraging challenging and radical new approaches to the medium

RAINBOW RADIO

A global radio station based in the UK and offering talk, oldies and African music. The station is based in Battersea and in Accra, Ghana.

UNITED DJs

A private online radio station staffed by former Radio Luxembourg DJs and run by that station's former Programme Manager, Tony Prince. The station is headquartered in the Thames Valley but most DJs broadcast direct from home; it's one of the most professional sounding stations to not have a traditional AM or FM outlet, but since 2018, UDJ has been heard on the Portsmouth mux and on the mux in Glasgow.

DAB & DAB+ The Future of Radio

Niocast Digital operates the Manchester small scale DAB+ multiplex. Its 25 digital radio stations are heard across the city reaching over 1 million people. It began operations in summer 2015 and has been 'fully subscribed' with a waiting list almost ever since. The stations now heard on its transmitter are:

Niocast also has its own mux management software called *Optimux*, which it offers free of charge for a year to new operators. Another sister company in the Niocast group is VIAMUX, described in Chapter 9 on suppliers, which provides a variety of support services to DAB multiplexes.

The company is run by David Duffy who is Operations Director and John Evington, head of Programming and Content. "Our new digital services cater for ethnic, lifestyle, specialist and general audiences across the city," says John.

Niocast have impressive expansion plans and, in partnership with local operators, hope to operate multiplexes in Sheffield, Cardiff, Edinburgh, Birmingham, Leeds and Bradford.

RADIO CAROLINE

A privately-owned radio station that began broadcasting in 1964 from a ship located in International Waters, because licences for private commercial stations were not available at that time. Within a week the station was attracting millions of listeners to its MW signal. Governments tried to stop it but Caroline continued until 1991 when it ran aground off Kent and her crew were rescued by helicopter.

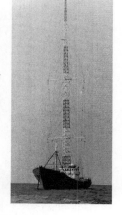

Caroline has since operated on satellite, online today now has an AM 'community of interest' licence in the east Anglia. It was one of the first stations to be heard digitally in the 1990s but has never been rich enough nor sufficiently well-organised to threaten commercial radio's big stations. Radio Caroline is the UK's longest running station to broadcast in DAB+.

The operators of some of the trial phase of muxes offered Caroline a slot, which the volunteers who now operate the station were happy to take up. Caroline's wide appeal and its legendary status has attracted many listeners to SS-DAB.

Radio Caroline can now be heard on DAB in several areas, as well as online and on 648AM over much of Europe.

The DAB muxes carrying Radio Caroline are:

| Brighton. | Portsmouth | Woking | Norwich |
| Cambridge | Manchester | Glasgow | London |

Further multiplexes hoping to launch in 2021 have already offered to carry the Radio Caroline service.

More details of Radio Caroline's exciting story can be found in the book telling the story of her days at sea and the battle for the station to broadcast on land. Details are on page 122.

DAB & DAB+ The Future of Radio

SMALL SCALE DAB MULTIPLEX LICENCES

These are designed to give an affordable and economically-viable route to DAB. This represents a major development for broadcasting; enabling small commercial operators and community stations to broadcast cost-effectively, and boosting listener choice.

In 2020, the UK regulator (OFCOM) began to offer small-scale DAB licences in eight batches, i.e up to 200 small-scale multiplexes over an extended period.

Round One included five areas where trials had been undertaken. 45 applicants applied to run multiplexes in the 25 locations offered:

MUX	APPLICANTS
Alnwick / Morpeth	CJ Broadcasting
	UK DAB Networks
Basingstoke	UK DAB Networks
Birmingham South	South Birmingham DAB
	South Birmingham Digital Radio
	UK DAB Networks
Bradford	Bradford Dab Network
	Bradford Digital Media
	Bradford Multiplex Broadcasting Corp
	Media Arts & Culture
Londonderry	Foyle DAB
Cambridge	Cambridge Digital Radio
Cardiff	Cardiff DAB
	Muxcast Three
Clevedon / Filton	Like DAB
	Severnside Digital Radio
Dudley	Boom Radio
	Digimux
	Dudley & Stourbridge DAB

DAB & DAB+ The Future of Radio

East Bristol	Bristol Digital Radio
Edinburgh	Edinburgh DAB Muxcast Two
Exeter	ExeDAB Like DAB
Glasgow	Nation Digital Investments
Inverclyde	UK DAB Networks
Isles of Scilly	Like DAB
Kings Lynn	North Norfolk Digital
Leeds	Boom Radio DAB Leeds Leeds DAB Radio Leeds Digital Media Tailor Made DAB for Leeds
Newcastle	Boom Radio Tyneside Community Digital
Birmingham North	Switch Radio
Norwich	Future Digital
Salisbury	Muxcast One
Sheffield & Rotherham	Media Arts & Culture Shefcast Digital Sheffield & Rotherham DAB
Tynemouth & South Shields	Mux One Muxcast Four
Welsh Valleys	GTFM (South Wales)
Winchester	UK DAB Network

ROUND TWO is due to be advertised in early 2021 and will cover areas in Lancashire, Cheshire and north east Wales. The areas to be offered for multiplexes are:

Manchester | Liverpool | Blackpool | Preston
Chester | Wrexham | Mid Cheshire | Wirral | Rhyl | Crewe
Glossop | Leek | Clitheroe | Bolton | Wigan | Oldham | Southport
Stockport | Warrington | East Cheshire | Stoke | Blackburn

An application fee of £500 is payable for a multiplex license. They must launch within eighteen months of the licence award, although most operators project a 4 to 6 months launch period. The multiplex licences are for seven years, renewable at the holder's option.

PROGRAMME LICENCES

Stations can apply for a programme licence at any time and operators don't need to align themselves with any one multiplex applicant before a licence is awarded, although the regulator does recommend that some dialogue take place early, to ensure carriage.

There are two Programme Licences available for station operators:
DSP (Digital Sound Programme)for regular stations, and
CDSP (Community Digital Sound Programme) for *not-for-profit*.

The DSP and C-DSPs are available at the same time as the multiplex licences are advertised. They allow stations to broadcast on the SSDAB and the regular local DAB multiplexes too. OFCOM aim to issue programme licences within four weeks of receiving applications. An Application Fee of £250 is payable for a programme licence, then an annual fee of £100 is charged for its renewal.

Each multiplex operator must ensure that a minimum number of slots, set by OFCOM, are available for community (C-DSP) licensees to be carried on the mux. In some areas this is only three, but in others it is high as eight.

LATEST INFORMATION

An up-to-date listing of every DAB station on the three national, the regional and local multiplexes as well as the Small Scale DAB muxes, can be found on the OFCOM web site: *www.ofcom.org*

LUMINARIES & LEADERS

The DAB business has such an assortment of bodies and organisations involved that it can be quite bewildering for listeners to know exactly who does what. We shall try and explain some of the key people involved in the world of DAB and the organisations with which they are involved.

It's been to the major institutes and companies who have played a vital role, or with whom ordinary listeners and those who are interested to discover the process of setting up a DAB station might encounter.

Ofcom
making communications work
for everyone

OFCOM

The UK regulator is in charge of all communications in the UK, including radio broadcasting, which it administers under the command of the DCMS.

OFCOM licences multiplex operators to provide the DAB transmission facilities and also licences programme providers, the radio stations. OFCOM's website (*www.ofcom.org.uk*) contains details of all the UK licensed DAB multiplexes.

DAB & DAB+ The Future of Radio

WorldDAB is the global industry forum for DAB digital radio. It facilitates the adoption and implementation of broadcast digital radio based on DAB, the digital radio standards of choice for broadcasters across Europe, Asia, the Pacific and beyond.

WorldDAB delivers tailored solutions and advice on all aspects of the switch from analogue to digital radio including regulation, licensing, technical trials, network build out, marketing and production of new digital radio content.

**WorldDAB's vision is for every person to
enjoy digital radio with DAB as its heart.**

The WorldDAB website contains information on DAB from all the countries that use the DAB standard. The website contains marketing resources for DAB stations and also documents setting out the arguments for DAB radio from many European countries, and Australia.

The website also sets out details of the DAB and DAB+ patents. (The European patents related to the DAB family of standards expired on 18th January 2013 and DAB is now a free-to-integrate technology).

The pressure on spectrum in the UHF band, where DTT is mainly implemented, has given rise to the idea that Band III could be used for DTT instead. This guide tells you why this is NOT the case and how you can contribute to the discussions. Several EBU Factsheets are found on the site, including a guide to the use of Band III, and the planning parameters for the band.

www.worlddab.org

OPENDAB

This is a not for profit company (a CIC) that provides essential knowledge for would-be operators and helps them to plan licence applications. Opendab organises the transmission infrastructure to make small scale DAB radio work efficiently and without fuss.

Opendab could be the licensed multiplex operator in any locality, combining its knowledge, experience and a transparent business approach with a station's vision.

Opendab is a 'non-profit distributing' CIC (Community Interest Company). Its directors and members are established figures in UK radio with long term experience of every aspect of public service, commercial and community broadcasting.

The Opendab team is led by **Daniel Nathan,** a launch consultant for London's Kiss 100 and co-founded Festival radio, one of the earliest trial stations in the UK licensed by the Home Office in the 1990s.

Daniel was a founder of *Spin-off Festival Productions* which made new music radio, ad campaigns, drama and documentaries for the BBC and UK commercial radio. Subsequently, he founded the Kiss FM station in in Manchester and later helped expand this to Yorkshire, as well as Brighton.

Daniel has been project leader for several key R&D projects, bringing together producers, aggregators, hardware manufacturers, broadcast and internet radio. In 2015 Daniel launched the UK's first open source 'DIY' broadcast digital radio multiplex.

DAB & DAB+ The Future of Radio

 **Dr Lawrie Hallet** has over 30 years of experience in broadcasting. A founder member of the Community Media Association and director of many broadcast companies, he has advised many successful licence applicants. He has helped to launch community services and commercial stations in the UK and elsewhere in Europe.

Between 2004 and 2012, Lawrie was a Senior Associate in Ofcom's Broadcast Radio Team, with specific responsibility for broadcast radio licensing and DAB planning and development. He is currently on the board of Future Digital Norfolk Limited, the trial small-scale DAB operator in Norwich and is a trustee of Future Projects Limited.

Paul Boon has been a radio campaigner, broadcaster, editor and regulator beginning as a newsreader on Radio Jackie in 1983. He chaired the Association for Broadcasting Development (ABD) a lobby group that successfully campaigned for more opportunities for new commercial and community radio stations.

Paul was the architect who brought about the award and launch of 26 new incremental radio stations in six months. He co-wrote winning radio licence applications and worked on several before joining *The Radio Magazine* where he became Managing Editor.

In 2008 Paul joined Ofcom for nine years working on commercial and community, analogue and digital radio projects as well as dealing with regulatory matters. Paul is now happy to lend his knowledge and support to the Opendab small-scale DAB project.

DAB & DAB+ The Future of Radio

Cᴍ Community Media
Association

Founded in 1983 as the Community Radio Association and, in 1997, became the Community Media Association to reflect the growing convergence of digital communications. It is a non-profit making organisation which represents the community media sector to Government, industry and regulatory bodies.

The membership brings together established organisations, aspirant groups and individuals within the sector. The CMA provides a range of advice, information and consultancy, offering support to anyone with an interest in the sector.

Much of the CMA's work has a strategic emphasis and the organisation has been intensely involved in liaison on behalf of the community broadcasting sector with Government, the regulator Ofcom and other strategic bodies regarding actual or proposed legislation and regulation of:

The CMA is based in Sheffield and is led by Operations Director, **Bill Best**. Bill has worked for the CMA since November 2000 having caught the community radio 'bug' while he was volunteering for the *Sheffield Live* RSL in July of that year.

Bill worked in IT Operations for HSBC Bank and his specialist areas are community broadcasting technologies, online media delivery, open source software solutions, and social media networks. Bill is an expert on licensing, music copyright and anything technical. He established and continues to develop the CMA's *Canstream* online media service.

The Radio Centre is the industry body of forty commercial radio operators who operate over 300 radio stations. These account for over 90% of the market by listening and in terms of revenue. The RadioCentre performs three main functions on behalf of its members:

ADVERTISING
RadioCentre promotes the benefits of radio to advertisers and agencies, asking them to see radio through a combination of marketing activity, research, and training.

POLICY
RadioCentre provides a collective voice on issues affecting the way that stations operate, working with government, politicians, policy makers and regulators to secure the best environment for growth and development of the medium.

CLEARANCE
RadioCentre ensures advertisements comply with the rules and standards laid out in the BCAP Code of Broadcast Advertising and the Ofcom Broadcasting Code.

The RadioCentre actively promotes radio advertising and DAB. It also organises the quarterly RAJAR radio audience measuring exercises, jointly with the BBC.

BITSTREAM BROADCAST
A Lancashire based consultancy providing everything from consultancy to system integration, at low cost. From a single transmitter to fully connected networks, FM, DTV and DAB. They can advise on planning, installation and ongoing maintenance. Bitstream are a small team of RF engineers, headed by ex-BBC and Arqiva engineer John Bibby. He was instrumental in the first DAB roll-outs over 25 years ago

Radio Listeners Guide

RLG publishes several very useful annual guides: The *Radio Listener's Guide*, the *Television Viewer's Guide* and the *Mobile Phone User's Guide*. They have been providing technology advice for over 20 years and take pride in providing well-researched, independent and up-to-date information and advice for consumers.

The annual **Radio Listener's Guide** contains a detailed analysis of the various broadcast stations and reception apparatus available to listeners in the UK market as well as giving a good appraisal of the trends in the radio business. The RPG also includes a listing of all the radio transmitters in the UK, including every known DAB transmitter and its power.

The Radio Listener's Guide is the UK's most detailed, comprehensive and independent guide to radio receivers, from portables up to the top of the range 'table top' and Hi Fi radios. These honest reviews are an invaluable guide for intending buyers plus the RLG also has news of the latest developments for listeners.

The 2021 guide has a section devoted to streaming and new technology, which covers Apps of use to radio listeners, the BBC Sounds operation, Spotify, Amazon Smart Speakers, multi-room systems such as *Sonos* , plus more general BlueTooth and music streaming services.

You can order Radio Listener Guide direct:-*www.radioguide.co.uk*

SMMT.

The Society of Motor Manufacturers and Traders is a trade body of about 800 companies in the car industry, with resources, reputation and unrivalled data about the UK automotive industry.

105

PAUL CHANTLER

A respected international broadcast consultant, providing valuable strategic, operational and training support. He has helped dozens of stations to launch and is an accomplished author – his book "Hang The DJ" provides essential help for presenters to avoid legal pitfalls.

Paul works in a variety of formats including Adult Contemporary, CHR, Hot AC, Dance, Christian, Sport and Newstalk. He has experience in radio presentation, production and programme management. In the 1990s, Paul was Group Programme Director for three of the UK's biggest radio groups.

Paul was responsible for launching two UK regional youth-format stations: *Galaxy* and *Vibe*, as well as helping to launch Ireland's speech station *NewsTalk* in 2002. He also ran UK national station *TalkSport* as Programme Director.

Paul is co-author of a highly-acclaimed and popular textbook on radio journalism, originally published 20 years ago, which has been translated into four languages and is in use in colleges throughout the world. He has also co-written two books on media law.

Radio Ideas Bank

The RADIO IDEAS BANK was founded by Paul Chantler. It is - an online service to make it easier for radio professionals to find ideas for contests and promotions which can be used to grow ratings and revenue. Paul is also brimming with ideas of new formats for radio stations and has been involved in many brainstorming sessions and station launches. Subjects and formats as unlikely as Podcast Radio and FIX RADIO , a station aimed at tradesmen and DIYers, are just two well-known examples of DAB stations he has spawned.

DAB & DAB+ The Future of Radio

QUENTIN HOWARD

One of the leading lights of the campaigners for DAB work is former ILR engineer **Quentin Howard**, FIET. A former ballet dancer, Quentin became the Chief Engineer at the GWR Group where he worked tirelessly to see the adoption of DAB and was appointed Chief Executive of the UK's first commercial radio multiplex, Digital One.

Quentin Howard FIET

Quentin was elected President of World DAB, the international promotional body for the standard. Quentin then served as CTO, Director of Television and Director of Strategy for BFBS, the British Forces Broadcasting Service, at their headquarters in Buckinghamshire. Whilst there he modernised the BFBS network and studios and ran Forces TV, the UK commercial TV channel. He is now an independent Broadcast and Media Consultant as well as podcaster and well known as "the Father of DAB." Quentin was for many years one of the biggest visionaries in radio, promising that the medium had a golden future, at a time when others predicted its demise.

Quentin was also the first UK broadcaster to present live radio programmes from home via ISDN with his music and phone-in show on Classic FM. He is also known as the creator of Classic FM's famous "Radio Birdsong" test transmissions which were later used on DAB for several years and are now available as a podcast. He has also appeared on many Podcasts, including the Birdsong one, as a guest host of Radio Today's Podcast and on several *Allergy Today* podcasts.

MEDIA SHOW

A weekly programme on BBC Radio 4 about all media, including social, anti-social and news, this occasionally mentions DAB. Claims to be a programme about a revolution in media, presented by Amol Rajan, the BBC's media editor. New episodes are released every Wednesday with previous editions being available to download on BBC Sounds.

 Podcast Radio showcases a variety of podcasts to the world, combining live presenters, news updates and charts. The Podcast Radio Network covers the entire digital audio ecosystem; pod-fans can now discover podcasts on their radios via DAB mux outlets in London, Surrey, Manchester and Glasgow.

The network, which is also available online via TuneIn, launched in early 2020 and is run by Gerry Edwards and was launched by Paul Chantler, the veteran radio consultant who has been a midwife at dozens of innovative station launches.

"Podcast Radio helps listeners discover and sample podcasts to find out which ones they like," explains Gerry. "For podcast producers, the channel is a showcase and shop window for their content. I've been a podcast enthusiast and evangelist for quite a few years and am excited to combining my love of podcasts with radio", he says.

RADIO TODAY
A publisher of news and comment about radio in the UK with regular podcasts and audio newsletters.

WORLDWIDE RADIO SUMMIT
Usually held in Hollywood every spring, brings together hundreds of radio broadcasters, record label executives, and other industry professionals. Lots of interviews with a wide range of speakers from the industry from CEOs to morning show hosts to consultants.

NAB PODCAST
Not so much DAB, though it's had a few mentions, but there is lots of news and comment about *HD Radio* and other digital radio developments. `Episodes are available to the public for a few weeks (you need to join the NAB to access them all).

Radioplayer

An online radio distribution platform owned by UK radio broadcasters and also operated under licence in some other countries. It offers stations an internet radio web tuner, a set of mobile phone apps, an in-car adaptor, and integrations with other connected devices and platforms. It's a non-profit organisation owned by its members, which include the BBC, Global, Bauer and the RadioCentre.

The UK Radio Player was launched in 2011 with 157 stations to offer a simple way to listen to radio stations via the internet. Though originally using the detested Flash software, the following year it became available on iPhones and on Android phones.

RadioPlayer now supports wearable gadgets, Apple Carplay, Android Auto and AppleWatch as well as being compatible with AirPlay and Chromecast. It can now be used with the Amazon's Echo, Sonos and the Bose multi-room speaker and has over five hundred stations available through it.

NATION BROADCASTING

One of the UK's fastest growing media companies, Nation is a portfolio of national, regional and local commercial radio stations, alongside a digital marketing business. Their radio stations reach almost a million adults listeners every week, in Wales, England and Scotland. Nation controls a number of Small Scale DAB muxes and local commercial operations as well as FM stations, in all three countries.

Nation is the lead investor in new DAB multiplexes in the Channel Islands, Lancashire and Cumbria, where they plan to introduce a new national brands and local stations.

www.nationbroadcasting.com

9. SUPPLIERS

BROADCAST RADIO

A company run by a team of expert staff with decades of experience both designing solutions and working in real radio stations. Founders Peter Jarrett and Liam Burke developed one of the first radio station software solutions while at Hull University in the early 1990s - **P-Squared**.

The P-Squared software has been the cornerstone of the playout system at many radio stations since its launch in 1997. It can now be found in over a thousand stations, from nationals right down to the smallest community outlets, who have all found its intuitive software among the easiest to learn.

The Yorkshire-based company has now expanded into many branches of broadcasting, meaning they can help guide you through both the technology and the creative process. *Broadcast Radio* offer bespoke complete 'turnkey' radio stations: studio design, and installation, software training, streaming and hosting services.

www.broadcastradio.com

AUDESSENCE

Involved in installing audio processors, transmission systems and STL links since 1984. The company is run by **Martin Spencer** and **Dr Lawrence Hallett;** they make and maintain audio processors (for all bands). *https://audessence.com*

AUDIO BROADCAST CONSULTANTS

A small, friendly bunch of experienced radio professionals offering independent advice. This is assured as they don't sell kit and so we are not encumbered by sales commissions when they make a recommendation. ABC specialise in FM radio transmission, but also have wide experience across the broadcast industry from studio specification to station imaging. Their expertise in coverage mapping is legendary and they have over 20 years' experience using computerised radio propagation modelling tools to quickly and accurately deliver radio coverage predictions / maps / plots.

Led by **Glyn and Clive Roylance** who have years of broadcast expertise and have been involved in exporting too. Glyn was a Broadcast Engineer at the IBA, and eventually with Arqiva, where he was responsible for installing, commissioning, operating and maintaining TV and radio networks like Capital Radio, LBC, BFBS, Channel 4 and ITV. He was personally involved in the "birth" of several stations: Jazz FM, Spectrum Radio and Choice FM.

Clive was involved in import /export before embarking on a radio career at the Voice of Peace "Somewhere in the Mediterranean". He set up and ran two stations in Ireland for many years with large AM and FM networks.

Clive enjoys radio presentation and is heard on voiceovers on several UK stations and catch him presenting on the legendary Radio Caroline each Sunday morning.

Commtronix

A leading DAB transmission consultancy, supplier and installer of everything needed to get a DAB station on air, Commtronix was founded by two former NTL and Arqiva engineers over ten years ago and has played a pivotal role in SSDAB since the launch in 2015. Firstly, with the Portsmouth trial, then Glasgow and then supplying equipment and knowledge to almost all of the other SSDAB operators.

Commtronix are one of the few UK companies involved with SSDAB to hold VIA licence patent agreement to distribute the patented aac+ coding software used for DAB+ and collect the associated royalties. They were the first to migrate SSDAB encoding from the OFCOM supplied systems onto lower cost raspberry pi's and brought innovations like slideshow onto several of the SSDAB muxes.

Offering a wide range of services for the broadcast and telecoms industry, from concept to commissioning, they cover the whole of the British Isles. Commtronix provide an end-to-end solution based on their 25 years of on-site practical experience of making radio happen. They offer transmission and multiplex install and maintenance to digital radio operators, as well as conventional AM and FM broadcasters and a wide range of network services including fibre optics.

Commtronix founders Alan Beech and Wallace McKeown each have experience of writing and implementing software test routines, debugging prototype commercial software, component level. They have worked on all manner of broadcast transmission and communications equipment, including the installation and commissioning of mega-watt diesel generators. There is not much in the world of communications and electronics engineering that they've not been involved with.

http://www.commtronix.co.uk

Viamux is a sister company of Niocast that provides small-scale DAB operators with help to win and operate a successful multiplex licence. Viamux also produce detailed coverage prediction maps and writes Ofcom licence applications.

The Viamux turn-key solution includes all the transmission equipment (antenna, amplifier, SDR and multiplex server) professionally installed at the transmission site(s). They provide hardware and windows DAB/DAB+ encoders - so that audio is encoded at the highest quality.

THEIR cloud facility encodes DAB and DAB+. Audio from client radio stations is encoded at their hub and 'blended' into a single multiplexed stream which is sent directly to the transmission site. Viamux can take care of the process of adding or removing programme services; managing carriage; monitoring alerts and providing status reports; as well as generating invoices and collecting carriage charges on the owner's behalf.

DIGITAL RADIO CHOICE
Digital Radio Choice is a buyer's guide for digital radios in the UK. Its website provides information about digital radios, answers to common questions and updates on programmes and stations. The aim of their website is to help buyers find the best new radios, etc, and it is funded by affiliate commissions they earn by referring buyers to radio retailers.

https://www.digitalradiochoice.com

RADIO STRUCTURES
A Northampton-based fabricator of masts and substructures since 1979. RS can also provide a rigging and installation service, from site surveys through to final installation. They also run training courses for mast climbers, to the strictest Arqiva safety standards. *www.radiostructures.com*

RADIO.CO

A Manchester-based company founded in 2015 by James Mulvany, Radio.co are a team that make radio for everyone. Specialising in online radio, they have helped many DAB stations too, with their own architecture, built completely from the ground up. James Mulvany, has been at the forefront of the internet radio industry for the past decade and has a large talented team of IT and programming experts. Radio.co train staff and offer cloud based systems to make it simple to launch micro radio stations. *www.radio.co*

Ebuyer

One of the largest online retailers of electronic components and equipment, they have over four million registered buyers and 250 staff. Its purpose built hub is just a few hundred yards from the M62 motorway, centrally located and ideal to ship to any UK or EU destination immediately. They hold vast stocks of computer equipment, peripherals and components. Ebuyer's philosophy is simple: "give the customers what they want, when they want it."

Check out Ebuyer's clearance lines: *https://tidd.ly/36En4wL*

Amazon

The biggest online retailer in the world, Amazon stock a wide range of DAB Radios, plus studio equipment and other items that listeners and broadcasters will find useful. The new *RodecasterPro* is a good example; now used by hundreds of broadcasters to make their programmes at home, it was supplied by the BBC to many of its team during lockdown. Amazon also have huge stocks of all the accessories found in the broadcast world. Direct link - *https://amzn.to/3kvXxdP*

Factum Radioscape

Software products include *Observa, Enmuxa*, etc, and cover the full digital radio broadcast signal chain: audio encoding, multiplexing, distribution and multiplex management, plus supervision, monitoring and analysis.

10. EPILOGUE

Ever since Baird first demonstrated television in the 1920s pessimists have predicted the end of radio. In recent decades is appeared as though they were right, when DAB's high prices and other difficulties seemed to be nails in radio's coffin. A combination of over-regulation, heartless management and zealous accountants were stifling the radio's creatives. Radio seemed to be gasping its last breath as its energy and enthusiasm was drained out of the medium, so loved by around 90% of the population for almost a hundred years.

Since its launch in the 1990s, DAB's advocates have stridently demanded that every AM, FM and other type of station be shut down, in order to give DAB a clear run at becoming the only type of sound broadcasting.

Fortunately, the authorities saw sense and didn't take such drastic action, which would consign hundreds of millions of perfectly useable radio receivers to landfill. A small group of pioneers developed an economic route to DAB and an enlightened regulator mapped out an alternative way to allow a couple of dozen small radio stations to broadcast. Those new stations have proven that radio doesn't need millions of pounds or the big corporate budgets to succeed.

Radio thrives on personality, on relevance to its listeners and opportunities for local people to influence their local stations, the grass roots where most national broadcasters take their first steps and learn their skills.

We are now on the cusp of a radio explosion with hundreds more radio stations about to be given the opportunity to show the service they can provide to listeners.

It's nothing less than a new dawn for radio.

Paul Rusling

11.   GLOSSARY

AAC   *Advanced Audio Coding* is a system of digital used in DAB+ and audio streaming. It is now the most widely used standard and was designed to be the successor to MP3. Usually heard as *aacPlus HE v2*.

ACI   Adjacent channel interference

AM.   *Amplitude Modulation*. Explained in Chapter1

APNG   *Animated Portable Network Graphics*, on DAB screens.

BANDS The electron-magnetic spectrum is divided up into bands of frequencies. The best known in broadcast radio terms are Medium Wave, Short Wave and the VHF broadcast Band II (88 to 108 MHz). DAB currently takes place in VHF Band III (174 – 240 MHz) and in the L Band (1.452 to 1.492 GHz).

BER   *Bit error rate* is calculated by comparing the transmitted sequence of bits to the received bits and counting the number of errors. The ratio of how many bits received in error over the number of total bits received is the BER.

CIR   *Channel Impulse Response* is one of the key criteria heard describing network performance,
especially when transmitter testing in SFN.

DAB   Digital Audio Broadcasting a digital radio encoding method.

DAB+   Newer DAB encoding system which makes more efficient use of the spectrum; squeezes more stations through the same transmitter at similar quality.

DAB & DAB+ The Future of Radio

DCMS   The *Digital, Culture, Media and Sport* ministry of the UK Government; they are responsible for broadcasting. The DCMS authorise OFCOM to manage the spectrum plus licensing of multiplex operators and radio stations.

DMB   *Digital Multimedia Broadcasting* - sometimes referred to as mobile TV. It's a sibling of DAB (Digital Audio Broadcasting) and DAB+.

DRM   *Digital Radio Mondial*, a system for adding digital signals in bands for analogue, e.g. MW, SW and FM

DSO   *Digital Switch Over.* – when analogue transmissions cease and digital becomes the sole transmission method.

EBU   *European Broadcasting Union*

EECC   *European Electronic Communications Code* An EU directive that makes it mandatory to install a digital radio receiver in every new car.

ENMUXA A complete DAB+ web-based software solution that includes encoders, multiplexing and system management,

Ensemble A group or a collection of radio stations. Ensemble is often used interchangeably with *multiplex*.

EPG   *Electronic Programme Guide*, an over the air menu.

ETSI   *European Transmission Standards Institute*

FM   *Frequency Modulation* – an analogue method of adding programme or data to a radio carrier.

FACTUM   Their RADIOSCAPE products cover the full digital radio broadcast signal chain, - audio encoding, data insertion, multiplexing, distribution and multiplex management, plus supervision, analysis, and a voice-break-in system for road tunnels.

FIC.   *Fast Information Channel.* A term used for signals with low data rates; e.g. paging, traffic info, or messaging.

FSK.   *Frequency Shift Keying.* A digital method of adding data to a radio signal.

GHz   *Giga Hertz.* One thousand million hertz. (10^9)

GSM   *Global System for Mobile communications.*

HE-AAC   *High Efficiency Advanced Audio Coding.*

ICE   *In Car entertainment,* which includes all kinds of audio equipment plus video and gaming too.

IP   (a) *Internet Protocol.* A unique address or method by which computers route data on the web.
             (b) *Intellectual Property* the rights to copyrights. an invention or patented work.

IRT   *Institute fur Rundfunk Technik* (the Institute for Broadcast Technology) based in Munich that invented DAB.

ISDN   *Integrated Services Digital Network.* A now obsolete standard of transmitting audio / data along lines.

ITU   *International Telecommunications Union* – Based in Geneva this is a global organisation whose membership is mainly communications and broadcast regulators from almost every nation in the world. It sets standards and agrees usage of the electro-magnetic spectrum.

Journaline A text based data service.

LSF   *Low Sampling Frequency* Low bitrate encoding with halved sampling rate.

M/bits   *Megabits* (10^6) *per second,* usually written *mbps*

MHz   *Megahertz,* one million (10^6) Hertz.

MER   *Modulation Error Rate* provides an indication on how well each symbol was received, often used in transmitter testing. MER is defined as the ratio of average symbol power to average error power. The optimum value should be at least 20dB, and never lower than 10dB.

DAB & DAB+ The Future of Radio

MiniMux a small multiplex (often applied to SS DAB).

MP3 Full Name *MPEG-1 Audio Layer III or MPEG-2 Audio Layer III* - it is a coding format for digital audio. Other coding formats include MP3, AAC, Vorbis, FLAC and Opus.

MPEG *Moving Picture Experts Group.* A working party of authorities in the audio, video, TV and radio industries to set standards for digital compression.

Multiplex a word describing the transmission of multiple radio stations or audio channels over a frequency.

MUX An abbreviation of the word **multiplex.**

MUXCO *Muxco* is a number of UK consortia who have been awarded local and regional DAB licences.

OBSERVA A DAB+ monitoring and analysis product from a London company called *Factum Radioscape.* It supervises, monitors, decodes and records a variety of transmission inputs.

OFCOM The UK regulator, authorised by DCMS to manage communications, including radio broadcasting.

OFDM *Orthogonal Frequency Division Multiplexing* is a type of digital transmissions, encoding data or programming onto several carriers, used in wideband transmission, such as DAB or TV.

PDM *Pulse Duration Modulation* a high efficiency technique used in high power AM transmission. A variation of PCM was called Pulse Step Modulation.

PSK *Phase shift keying*, a digital modulation process used for data transmission.

QAM *Quadrature Amplitude Modulation* is several methods of applying digital modulation to a carrier. Two feeds are added to the carrier, out of phase.

RDS   *Radio Data System.* A method of adding information and data to an FM broadcast signal. Used for Station Identification, the time and limited programme information.

RF   *Radio Frequency.* Usually applied to an electro-magnetic wave (radio energy). From16KHz up.

SCADA   Supervisory control and data acquisition,

SDL   *Sound Digital Ltd* is the operator of the UK's second 'national' network, reaching 83% of the population.

SLIDESHOW A feature to add graphics and other visual content (slides) to a receiver's screen via DAB / DAB+ transmissions.

SDR   *Software Defined Radio* – a complete radio receiver in a box, plugged into a computer for demodulating.

SFN   *Single Frequency Network.*

SMMT   A trade body for the UK automotive industry. Members include those involved in ICE.

TPEG   Protocol suite used to transmit traffic information on DAB.

VHF   Part of the Spectrum from 30 to 300 Megahertz, (1 to 10M)

UHF   Part of the Spectrum from 300 to 3000 Megahertz.

VIA   An Intellectual Property solutions company who manage licence and royalty payments for patents.

VQ   British radio brand established by Jonathan Merricks in 2011, originally called *ViewQuest.* They manufactured the original retro radio, which also had an iPod dock.

RADIO FORMATS

in the UK and US

A fascinating new book in 2020, describing the evolution of radio station formats on both sides of the pond over the last hundred years.

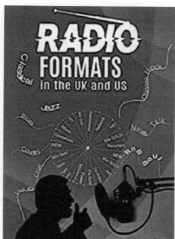

Radio Formats in the UK and ***US*** tells how speech and music radio in the USA followed public demand into sharply defined streams, following music genres. It also describes how the radio landscape in the UK was stifled by regulators.

Over 130 radio formats are described in the books 100 pages. It guides readers through radio's halcyon days, highlighting some of the milestones of broadcasting and introduces the pioneers who developed particular formats. The UK's BBC stations (national, regional and local) are covered as are commercial stations, community radio and both onshore and offshore pirates.

More details about the book and ordering links are at:

https://WorldofRadio.co.uk/RadioFormats.html

For a range of books about the radio industry, visit

https://WorldofRadio.co.uk/RadioBooks.html

The Radio Caroline Bible

The full story of how the world's most famous offshore radio ship attracted millions of listeners but finally came ashore and is a part of the UK's burgeoning DAB Network. Radio Caroline is now the longest running station using the DAB+ standard.

The RADIO CAROLINE BIBLE tells the story of the station's life and explains many previously untold aspects from the point of view of those who were there. With input from key Radio Caroline team members, the book tells chronologically what really happened around the start of the project, the fund-raising process, who put up the money, why and what was the legal basis for the station.

The full story of Radio Caroline's sixties operation, the difficulties that led to the ships being towed away and the mystery man really paid to set the Mi Amigo free once again. Dutch contracts, Caroline Homes, two government raids – all the details are in here.

The story is brought right up to date with Caroline's Chinese connection, the motor racing links, the relaunch using the former BBC World Service site and channel plus Caroline Flashback, the new community Caroline station in Essex and another new boat! This hardback book is indexed and illustrated with over 300 black and white photographs; a story that will keep you amused and amazed for hours.

See the book's own website for fuller details:
https://RadioCarolineBible.com

ABOUT THE AUTHOR

Paul Rusling studied radio engineering in the early 1970s, financed by working as disc jockey in night clubs. In 1973 he joined *Radio Caroline* as a disc jockey and hosted the station's breakfast programme.

Paul and his wife Anne managed nightclubs and pubs in London and the south for some years before working as a broadcast consultant. In 1983, he converted a research ship, the MV Communicator, for use as a floating radio station. Best known as *Laser 558*, which attracted ten million listeners, the ship hosted eleven radio stations in its radio career.

Paul's work as a broadcast consultant saw him involved in 18 successful licence applications, mostly for large scale, national radio stations, in several countries. His work has often included programming and engineering, combined with management functions. He has also worked as a consultant to media regulators as well as for both state and private stations, including *Sky, Virgin*, the *SBC*, *RTL* and *Classic FM*.

Paul has written many articles on radio and other media for magazine and periodicals and has had several books published about radio. Recent books have described how to build and operate an online radio station, and how radio formats developed in the UK and US. Other books have been about specific radio stations, or training manuals.

Enquiries to *WBC@Worldofradio.co.uk*

Printed in Great Britain
by Amazon

54496628R00070